# Answer Keys

**This book was printed with acid-free recycled content paper, containing 10% POSTCONSUMER WASTE.**

## HOLT, RINEHART AND WINSTON

A Harcourt Classroom Education Company

**Austin** • New York • Orlando • Atlanta • San Francisco • Boston • Dallas • Toronto • London

# Holt Science Spectrum: A Physical Approach

**Answer Keys**

Printed in the United States of America

ISBN 0-03-055593-0

4 5    862    04 03 02

**Cover:** basketball image: David Madison/Tony Stone Images; celestial background image: Corbis Images **Photo Credits:** All photos Sam Dudgeon/HRW Photo

# CONTENTS

# Answer Keys

Study Guide Answer Key. . . . . . . . . . . . . . . . . . . . . . . . . . 1
Math Skills Answer Key. . . . . . . . . . . . . . . . . . . . . 27
Integration Worksheets Answer Key . . . . . . . . . . . . . . . 43
Basic Skills Answer Key . . . . . . . . . . . . . . . . . . . . 63
Lesson Focus Answer Key . . . . . . . . . . . . . . . . . . . . 71

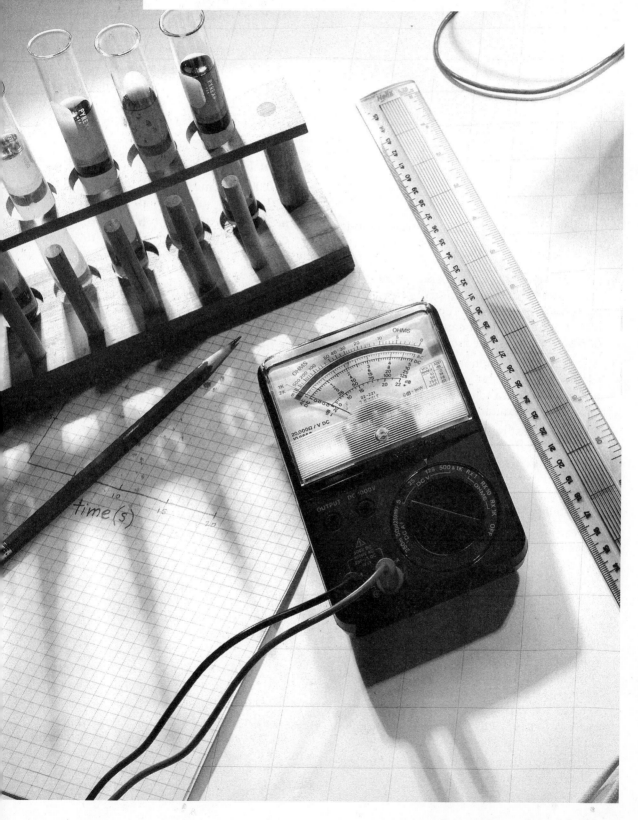

# STUDY GUIDE
# ANSWER KEY

# STUDY GUIDE ANSWER KEY

## Chapter 1
### Introduction to Science

#### PRETEST

1. a
2. d
3. a
4. **a.** mass **b.** volume **c.** time **d.** length **e.** temperature **f.** area **g.** length **h.** volume **i.** mass **j.** area
5. c
6. **a.** 4.5 m$^2$
   $A = lw = (3.0 \text{ m})(1.5 \text{ m}) = 4.5 \text{ m}^2$
   **b.** 54 m$^3$
   $V = lwh = (3.0 \text{ m})(1.5 \text{ m})(12 \text{ m}) = 54 \text{ m}^3$

#### SECTION 1.1

1. Answers may vary. Possible answers include botany, zoology, medicine, agriculture, marine biology, and physiology.
2. **a.** a system of knowledge based on facts or principles **b.** the application of science to meet human needs **c.** a representation of an object or an event that can be studied to understand the real object or event
3. A scientific law summarizes an observed natural event without offering an explanation for it, while a scientific theory provides a possible explanation of a natural event.
4. Scientists must be objective in their observations so that their observations are accurate. If scientists only make observations that support a particular theory, they may overlook important observations that contradict their theory.
5. **a.** Scientists carefully plan experiments so that they will answer a particular question. **b.** Scientists repeat experiments to make sure that their results are accurate and can be duplicated.

#### SECTION 1.2

1. Answers may vary. Answers might include microscopes (used to magnify very small objects or the details of larger objects), telescopes (used to magnify distant objects, such as stars and galaxies), and particle accelerators (used to study the structure of atoms and the parts of atoms).
2. If more than one variable is tested, it is difficult to draw a definite conclusion from the results.

3. **a.** 0.95 m **b.** 1100 mL **c.** 17 km **d.** 500 000 g **e.** 0.002 55 mol **f.** 275 000 000 A
4. The original hypothesis may not be supported by experimental results. The experiment may point to a new, more specific hypothesis.
5. Prefixes make it easy to express very large or very small numbers.
6. The SI units are used by scientists all over the world so that all scientists understand the data regardless of who generated the data.

#### SECTION 1.3

1. **a.** 0.002 54 cm    **b.** 95 000 km
   **c.** 0.33 L    **d.** 744.5 g
2. **a.** $3.25 \times 10^2$ kg    **b.** $4.6 \times 10^{-4}$ m
   **c.** $7.104 \times 10^3$ km    **d.** $2.8 \times 10^{-3}$ L
3. **a.** 3    **b.** 4
   **c.** 6    **d.** 5
4. **a.** $3.8 \times 10^6$ cm$^2$    **b.** $2.06 \times 10^8$ km$^2$
   **c.** $5.8 \times 10^{-4}$    **d.** $3 \times 10^4$ m/s
5. The data points might be located close together indicating precision, but they might not be close to the true value.
6. All data is displayed side-by-side on the same graph for easy comparison.

#### CHAPTER 1 MIXED REVIEW

1. **a.** high precision, low accuracy **b.** low precision, low accuracy **c.** high precision, high accuracy **d.** low precision, high accuracy
2. Mass is a measure of the quantity of matter in an object. Weight is the force on the object due to gravity. So mass is constant regardless of location, while weight is not.
3. Answers will vary. Check that students list steps of the scientific method: ask a question, collect data, form a hypothesis, test the hypothesis, draw conclusions, and modify the hypothesis.
4. Answers may vary. Sample answer: A scientist could build a model of a new airplane and test it in a wind tunnel to see how air flows over the airplane's body and wings.
5. A line graph is best to display a runner's speed because the runner's speed will probably change over time. Line graphs are good representations of cases with an independent variable and a dependent variable.

**6. a.** $2.52 \times 10^4$ m  **b.** $1 \times 10^{-3}$ Mg
   **c.** $5.99 \times 10^{-4}$ L  **d.** 7.89 ms

**7.** Students should draw a pie chart. Check students' drawings for accuracy.

**8. a.** length  **b.** volume  **c.** the quantity of matter in an object  **d.** the space occupied by an object  **e.** meter  **f.** kilogram

# Chapter 2
## Matter
### PRETEST

**1.** a, b, c, e

**2.** d

**3.** b

**4.** a

**5.** a

**6.** a

**7. a.** $5 \times 10^{-3}$ g  **b.** $2.34 \times 10^4$ s
   **c.** $6.7 \times 10^2$ L  **d.** $3.2 \times 10^2$ °C
   **e.** $8.9 \times 10^{-4}$ m

### SECTION 2.1

**1. a.** heterogeneous  **b.** homogeneous
   **c.** heterogeneous  **d.** heterogeneous
   **e.** heterogeneous  **f.** homogeneous

**2.** An atom is the smallest particle that has the properties of an element, while a molecule is the smallest unit of a substance that has the properties of that substance. Molecules consist of two or more atoms chemically joined together.

**3.** A pure substance is made up of matter that has a fixed composition and definite properties. Although a homogeneous mixture is uniformly mixed, it is a combination of more than one pure substance and does not necessarily have a fixed composition.

**4. a.** compound  **b.** element
   **c.** compound  **d.** element
   **e.** compound  **f.** element

**5.** Elements are pure substances because each has a fixed composition of protons, neutrons, and electrons and particular characteristic properties. Compounds are pure substances because each has a fixed composition of atoms and definite properties.

**6. a.** mixture  **b.** pure substance
   **c.** pure substance  **d.** pure substance
   **e.** mixture  **f.** mixture

### SECTION 2.2

**1. a.** liquid  **b.** gas  **c.** solid

**2. a.** added  **b.** fastest  **c.** vaporization/evaporation  **d.** absorbed  **e.** slow down  **f.** condensation  **g.** released

**3.** The sugar molecules will have a lower speed on average than the water molecules because the sugar molecules are more massive than the water molecules. As the temperature of the mixture increases, the speed of all of the molecules will increase.

**4.** c

**5.** The total number of water molecules, and therefore the mass, stays the same; the molecules are just spread out over a greater volume. Energy is transferred from the surroundings to the water, so the water molecules are moving faster than they were, but the total amount of energy is the same.

### SECTION 2.3

**1. a.** physical property  **b.** chemical property
   **c.** physical property  **d.** physical property
   **e.** chemical property

**2. a.** physical property  **b.** chemical property
   **c.** physical property  **d.** physical property
   **e.** physical property

**3. a.** physical change  **b.** chemical change
   **c.** physical change  **d.** physical change
   **e.** chemical change  **f.** chemical change

**4.** 136.3 g silver
   $m = DV = (10.49 \text{ g/cm}^3)(12.99 \text{ cm}^3) = 136.3$ g

**5.** 2.3 g/cm$^3$
   $D = m/V = (820 \text{ g})/(350 \text{ cm}^3) = 2.3$ g/cm$^3$

**6.** Some of the food mass is digested and becomes part of your body cells and some of the food mass becomes waste, but the total amount of mass stays the same. Energy stored in the food molecules is released and transferred to your body when the food molecules are digested. The energy might be converted between different forms, but the total amount of energy stays the same.

### CHAPTER 2 MIXED REVIEW

**1.** Both elements and compounds have fixed compositions and definite properties. Both are the smallest amount of a particular substance that has the properties of that substance. However, compounds contain atoms of different elements that are bonded together and can be broken down into the elements they are made of.

**2.** Answers may vary. Sample answers might include the following: determining its density, melting point, boiling point, or conductivity.

3. If the two miscible liquids have different boiling points, they can be separated by distillation. Because the two immiscible liquids do not dissolve in each other, they will stay separated. They will not need to be separated by distillation.

4. The molecules that are fragrant will move faster at a higher temperature than they do at a lower temperature. The molecules will spread out and be in a larger volume, so there will be more opportunities for the molecules to be in the air that is inhaled.

5. When a substance undergoes a physical change, only its physical properties change. When a substance undergoes a chemical change, both its chemical and physical properties change.

6. $0.46 \text{ g/cm}^3$
$D = m/V = (31 \text{ g})/(68 \text{ cm}^3) = 0.46 \text{ g/cm}^3$

7. $4.01 \times 10^4 \text{ g}$
$m = DV = (7.265 \text{ g/cm}^3)(5.5 \text{ L})$
$\quad (1000 \text{ mL/L})(1 \text{ cm}^3/\text{mL}) = 4.01 \times 10^4 \text{ g}$

8. $2.53 \times 10^4 \text{ cm}^3$
$V = \dfrac{m}{D} = \dfrac{(25.3 \text{ kg})(1000 \text{ g/kg})}{1.00 \text{ g/cm}^3} = 2.53 \times 10^4 \text{ cm}^3$

9. **a.** pure substances **b.** mixtures
**c.** heterogeneous **d.** chemical properties
**e.** physical properties **f.** reactivity
**g.** density

# Chapter 3
## Atoms and the Periodic Table
### Pretest

1. c

2. **a.** element **b.** element **c.** compound
**d.** element **e.** element **f.** compound

3. **a.** mixture **b.** pure substance **c.** pure substance **d.** mixture

4. Helium-filled balloons and hot-air balloons are less dense than the surrounding air. Therefore, they float in the air.

5. $D = m/V = (157 \text{ g})/(412 \text{ cm}^3) = 0.381 \text{ g/cm}^3$
Yes, this substance would float on water because its density is less than the density of water ($1.0 \text{ g/cm}^3$).

6. c

## Section 3.1

1. Check students' drawings. Drawings should include two protons and two neutrons clustered in the nucleus and two electrons moving around outside the nucleus. Protons have a +1 charge, electrons have a −1 charge, and neutrons have a charge of zero.
proton mass $= 1.67 \times 10^{-27} \text{ kg}$
electron mass $= 9.11 \times 10^{-31} \text{ kg}$
neutron mass $= 1.67 \times 10^{-27} \text{ kg}$

2. Dalton proposed that each element is made up of unique atoms that cannot be subdivided, that all of the atoms of an element are the same, and that atoms from different elements join together to form molecules.

3. The outermost electrons of an atom have greater energy than the innermost electrons of an atom.

4. In both theories, electrons orbit the nucleus and each electron has an energy level associated with its location. In Bohr's model of the atom, electrons were thought to orbit the nucleus in set paths, much like planets orbiting the sun. In the modern atomic theory, the region in an atom where electrons are likely to be found is called an orbital. But the exact location of an electron cannot be determined according to this model.

## Section 3.2

1. **a.** Mn **b.** Pb **c.** C **d.** U **e.** Rn **f.** Ag

2. Atoms of elements that have the same number of valence electrons are located in the same group (column) of the periodic table.

3. The atomic number is the number of protons found in the nucleus of an atom. The mass number is the total number of protons plus neutrons found in the nucleus.

4. Atoms of Group 1 elements lose the one valence electron they have to form cations with a full outermost energy level. Atoms of Group 17 elements have seven valence electrons and gain one electron to form anions with a full outermost energy level.

5.

| Isotope | Symbol | p | n | e⁻ |
|---|---|---|---|---|
| protium | $_1^1\text{H}$ | 1 | 0 | 1 |
| deuterium | $_1^2\text{H}$ | 1 | 1 | 1 |
| tritium | $_1^3\text{H}$ | 1 | 2 | 1 |

**6.** The average atomic mass of hydrogen is listed in the periodic table as 1.01 amu. This value is closest to the atomic mass of protium (the most common hydrogen isotope), which has an atomic mass of about 1.0 amu (one proton and no neutrons).

## SECTION 3.3

**1. a.** alkali metal **b.** semiconductor **c.** transition metal **d.** alkaline-earth metal **e.** transition metal **f.** semiconductor

**2. a.** other nonmetal **b.** halogen **c.** noble gas **d.** other nonmetal **e.** noble gas **f.** halogen

**3. a.** no **b.** no **c.** yes **d.** yes **e.** no **f.** no

**4.** Chlorine is reactive because it needs to gain only one more electron to have a full outermost energy level. Argon is not reactive because it has a full outermost energy level.

**5. a.** similar **b.** similar **c.** different **d.** similar, both unreactive **e.** different

## SECTION 3.4

**1.** A mole is $6.022 \times 10^{23}$ particles.

**2. a.** yes **b.** no **c.** yes **d.** yes

**3.** A large counting unit like the mole is used to count atoms because atoms are too small to count individually.

**4. a.** 40.08 g/mol    **b.** 58.93 g/mol
**c.** 32.07 g/mol    **d.** 16.00 g/mol

**5.** List the given and unknown values. Write down the form of the molar mass that will convert moles to grams (grams in the numerator, moles in the denominator). Multiply the amount of the element by the conversion factor, and solve.

**6. a.** 12 g of Ne    **b.** 658 g of Xe
**c.** 150 g of Se    **d.** 650 g of Au

**7. a.** 0.35 mol of H    **b.** 37.5 mol of B
**c.** 0.50 mol of Cr    **d.** 0.26 mol of S

## CHAPTER 3 MIXED REVIEW

**1.** The average atomic mass of an element is close to a whole number if one of the element's isotopes is much more abundant than the other isotopes of that element. Also, some elements have only one isotope, so their average atomic masses will be very close to whole numbers.

**2. a.** 8 protons, 10 electrons, 8 valence electrons **b.** 54 protons, 54 electrons, 8 valence electrons **c.** 20 protons, 18 electrons, 8 valence electrons **d.** 11 protons, 10 electrons, 8 valence electrons

**3. a.** alkaline-earth metals (Group 2), 2 valence electrons, Be, Mg, Ca, Sr, Ba, Ra **b.** alkali metals (Group 1), 1 valence electron, Li, Na, K, Rb, Cs, Fr **c.** noble gases (Group 18), 8 valence electrons, He, Ne, Ar, Kr, Xe, Rn **d.** halogens (Group 17), 7 valence electrons, F, Cl, Br, I, At

**4.** Elements in the same family, or group, have the same number of valence electrons and therefore have similar reactivities.

**5.** There are more atoms in 100 g of neon ($3 \times 10^{24}$ neon atoms) than in 100 g of gold ($3 \times 10^{23}$ gold atoms). There are more protons in 100 g of neon ($3 \times 10^{24}$ neon atoms $\times$ 10 protons/neon atom = $3 \times 10^{25}$ protons) than in 100 g of gold ($3 \times 10^{23}$ gold atoms $\times$ 79 protons/gold atom = $2 \times 10^{25}$ protons).

**6. a.** 140 g of Ag    **b.** 111 g of Rn
**c.** 79.8 g of Sn    **d.** 140 g of Ca

**7. a.** 1.76 mol of Zn    **b.** 0.716 mol of Cu
**c.** 4.01 mol of Fe    **d.** 26.7 mol of He

**8. a.** cations **b.** protons **c.** electrons **d.** nucleus

# Chapter 4
## The Structure of Matter
### PRETEST

**1.** A chemical property describes the way in which a substance reacts to form new substances with different properties. A physical property is a characteristic of a substance that can be observed or measured without changing the composition of the substance.

**2.** A mixture consists of more than one pure substance.

**3.** Alkali metals are not found in nature as elements because they are extremely reactive.

**4.** Cations are positively charged ions formed by an atom losing one or more electrons. Anions are negatively charged ions formed by an atom gaining one or more electrons.

**5.** c

**6. a.** 2 nitrogen atoms **b.** 2 hydrogen atoms, 1 oxygen atom **c.** 2 carbon atoms, 6 hydrogen atoms, 1 oxygen atom **d.** 12 carbon atoms, 22 hydrogen atoms, 11 oxygen atoms

**7. a.** nonmetal **b.** metal **c.** nonmetal **d.** metal **e.** metal

### SECTION 4.1

**1.** Separating the elements of a compound is harder because the bonds between the atoms must be broken.

**2.** **a.** 1 sodium cation, 1 chloride anion
  **b.** 1 carbon atom, 2 oxygen atoms
  **c.** 1 potassium cation, 1 bromide anion
  **d.** 1 nitrogen atom, 3 hydrogen atoms
  **e.** 1 magnesium cation, 1 oxide anion

**3.** A ball-and-stick model gives you a better idea of bond lengths and bond angles. A space-filling model gives you a better idea of the space occupied by atoms.

**4.** Substances with network structures have strong bonds holding the atoms or ions together. Much energy (a higher temperature) is needed to break these bonds.

**5.** Table salt has a strong network structure consisting of very tightly bonded sodium cations and chloride anions. Table sugar is made of individual molecules. The bonds within each molecule are strong, but there are no bonds (just slight attractions) between molecules.

**6.** Because the boiling point of the compound is relatively low, the compound is likely to be in the form of individual molecules.

## SECTION 4.2

**1.** Solid ionic compounds, like table salt, do not conduct electricity because of the strong attractions locking the ions in place. When an ionic compound is dissolved in water, the charged ions are free to move so that the solution can conduct electricity.

**2.** Table salt does not melt easily because the attractions between sodium ions and chloride ions are very strong, requiring a great deal of energy to break.

**3.** An ionic bond is formed by the attraction between oppositely charged ions. A covalent bond is formed when atoms share one or more pairs of electrons.

**4.** A triple bond is stronger than a double bond because 3 pairs of electrons are shared to form a triple bond, while only 2 pairs of electrons are shared to form a double bond.

**5.** A compound that contains one or more polyatomic ions has both ionic and covalent bonds. The atoms making up the polyatomic ion are covalently bonded. The polyatomic ion forms an ionic bond with an oppositely charged ion.

**6.** Gold has metallic bonds in which the electron clouds of the gold atoms overlap. This overlap allows electrons to be transferred from atom to atom easily; therefore, gold is a good conductor of electricity.

## SECTION 4.3

**1.** The charge of the iron ions in each compound is different. The Roman numeral shows that iron(II) nitrate contains $Fe^{2+}$ ions while iron(III) nitrate contains $Fe^{3+}$ ions.

**2.** **a.** titanium(IV) oxide **b.** barium chloride **c.** copper(III) chloride **d.** potassium iodide **e.** strontium chloride **f.** copper(II) bromide

**3.** A prefix is added to the name of the first element telling how many atoms of that element are in one molecule (unless there is only one atom). A prefix is also added to the name of the second element telling how many atoms of that element are in one molecule. In addition, the ending of the second element is replaced with the suffix *-ide*.

**4.** **a.** $N_2O_5$ **b.** $CO$ **c.** $CCl_4$ **d.** $NF_3$ **e.** $PCl_5$ **f.** $S_2Cl_2$

**5.** The empirical formula for a compound tells the smallest whole-number ratio of atoms making up a molecule or formula unit of a compound. The molecular formula for a compound reports the actual numbers of atoms there are in one molecule of the compound.

## SECTION 4.4

**1.** **a.** alcohol **b.** alkene **c.** alcohol **d.** alkane **e.** alkene **f.** alkane

**2.** An alkane is an organic compound that has only single bonds between carbon atoms. Examples of alkanes are methane, ethane, and propane. An alkene is an organic compound that has at least one double bond between two carbon atoms. An alkene may also have single bonds between other carbon atoms. Examples of alkenes are ethene, propene, and butene.

**3.** Alcohol molecules ($CH_3$—OH or $C_2H_6$—OH) are similar to water molecules (H—OH) except that a hydrogen atom is replaced by a different group (i.e., a methyl, ethyl, or some similar group). Also, both alcohol molecules and water molecules have attractions between their molecules.

**4.** Starch is a polymer consisting of many bonded glucose molecules.

**5.** carbon, hydrogen, oxygen, nitrogen, and sulfur

**6.** Adenine always pairs with thymine. Cytosine always pairs with guanine.

## CHAPTER 4 MIXED REVIEW

1. The solution would be a mixture because the residue indicates that something else was dissolved in the liquid.

2. **a.** alkane **b.** -*ane* **c.** double covalent bond between two carbon atoms **d.** -*ene* **e.** alcohol **f.** contains a hydroxyl group (—OH)

3. **a.** metallic **b.** ionic **c.** covalent

4. Proteins in your body are polymers that are made from the amino acids that are broken down from proteins that you eat.

5. **a.** methane **b.** copper(III) iodide **c.** aluminum chloride **d.** diphosphorus pentoxide **e.** ethanol

6. The carbon atoms in a diamond are arranged in a crystal network structure that makes diamonds very strong. The carbon atoms in graphite are not in a network structure, so they are weakly held together.

7. Carbon atoms and hydrogen atoms can combine in many different ways—they can be branched and unbranched, or may even form rings.

8. **a.** bonds **b.** ionic bonds **c.** covalent bonds **d.** metallic bonds **e.** ions **f.** polyatomic ions

# Chapter 5
## Chemical Reactions
### PRETEST

1. **a.** covalent **b.** metallic **c.** ionic **d.** covalent **e.** covalent **f.** ionic

2. **a.** silver nitrate **b.** methanol **c.** potassium chloride **d.** benzene **e.** carbon monoxide **f.** sodium hydroxide

3. Mass cannot be created or destroyed.

4. b

5. Chemical changes are changes in the composition of a substance, while physical changes are changes in the physical form or properties of a substance without a change in the composition of the substance.

6. Energy cannot be created or destroyed.

### SECTION 5.1

1. **a.** reactants: $Fe_2O_3$ and Al; products: Fe and $Al_2O_3$ **b.** reactants: $AgNO_3$ and $H_2SO_4$; products: $Ag_2SO_4$ and $HNO_3$

2. When the natural gas burns, the bonds in the molecule are broken and the energy is released as heat.

3. energy is released as light, heat, or sound: examples may include the flame produced by a match when it is struck; the production of a gas: examples may include how carbon dioxide is produced when bread is rising; a change in color: examples may include that apples turn brown when exposed to air

4. sodium, carbon, oxygen, and hydrogen

5. Energy is transferred to the reactants from the surroundings in an endothermic reaction. Energy is transferred to the surroundings from the reactants in an exothermic reaction.

6. **a.** Hg and $O_2$ **b.** Ag and $O_2$

### SECTION 5.2

1. oxygen

2. A single-replacement reaction will have one compound and one element as reactants and one compound and one element as products, while a double-replacement reaction has two compounds as reactants and two compounds as products.

3. Electrons are transferred between elements during the reaction. The substance that gains electrons is reduced and the substance that loses electrons is oxidized.

4. **a.** Ag is reduced, Cu is oxidized **b.** Cu is reduced, Al is oxidized

5. **a.** combustion **b.** synthesis **c.** double-displacement **d.** single-displacement **e.** decomposition

6. Synthesis reactions join substances to make a new, more complex compound. Decomposition reactions break a compound into at least two products. In combustion reactions, a substance reacts with oxygen. In single-replacement reactions, atoms of one element appear to take the place of atoms of another element in a compound. In double-replacement reactions, ions appear to be exchanged between compounds, producing a gas, a solid precipitate, or a molecular compound.

### SECTION 5.3

1. **a.** $N_2O_5 + H_2O \rightarrow 2HNO_3$
   **b.** $2Fe(OH)_3 \rightarrow Fe_2O_3 + 3H_2O$
   **c.** $4Fe + 3O_2 \rightarrow 2Fe_2O_3$
   **d.** $2Al + 3CuSO_4 \rightarrow Al_2(SO_4)_3 + 3Cu$
   **e.** $2NaCl + H_2SO_4 \rightarrow Na_2SO_4 + 2HCl$

**2.** The mole ratio for $C:O_2:CO$ is $2:1:2$. (balanced equation is $2C + O_2 \rightarrow 2CO$)

**3.** 2 mol NaOH (balanced equation is $2Na + 2H_2O \rightarrow 2NaOH + H_2$)

**4.** 68 g CO
($78$ g $CH_3OH$) (mol $CH_3OH/32$ g) = $2.4$ mol $CH_3OH$
($2.4$ mol CO)($28$ g CO/mol CO) = 68 g CO

**5.** Each side of the equation has three sodiums, seven oxygens, six hydrogens, and one phosphorus. Because both sides have the same number of atoms of each element, mass is conserved.

## SECTION 5.4

**1.** If a change is made to a system in chemical equilibrium, the equilibrium shifts to oppose the change until a new equilibrium is reached.

**2.** Answers may vary. The table salt can be ground up into small particles. The temperature of the water can be increased.

**3. a.** toward the left   **b.** toward the right
   **c.** toward the right   **d.** toward the right

**4. a.** toward the left   **b.** toward the right
   **c.** toward the right   **d.** toward the right

## CHAPTER 5 MIXED REVIEW

**1.** A refrigerator cools food. Decreasing the temperature reduces the rate of the chemical reactions that spoil food.

**2. a.** reactant: silver chlorate, $AgClO_3$; products: silver chloride, AgCl, and oxygen, $O_2$
   **b.** $AgClO_3 \rightarrow AgCl + O_2$
   **c.** $2AgClO_3 \rightarrow 2AgCl + 3O_2$

**3. a.** AB, synthesis  **b.** A + B, decomposition
   **c.** AY + BX, double-replacement  **d.** A + BX, single-replacement

**4.** When each side in a game of tug-of-war is pulling and being pulled the same amount, neither side is moving and both sides are at a standstill. A chemical reaction at equilibrium is similar because the rates of the forward and reverse reactions are identical, so the amounts of reactants and products does not change.

**5. a.** water, $H_2O$, and carbon dioxide, $CO_2$
   **b.** released  **c.** The energy is stored in the bonds of the reactants and is released when those bonds are broken.

**6. a.** equations  **b.** equilibrium  **c.** catalyst
   **d.** balanced  **e.** enzyme

# Chapter 6
## Solutions, Acids, and Bases
### PRETEST

**1. a.** heterogeneous      **b.** heterogeneous
   **c.** homogeneous      **d.** homogeneous
   **e.** homogeneous

**2. a.** solid  **b.** gas  **c.** solid  **d.** liquid  **e.** solid

**3.** photosynthesis, respiration, combustion

**4.** b

**5. a.** $2Fe(OH)_3 \rightarrow Fe_2O_3 + 3H_2O$
   **b.** $2NaCl + H_2SO_4 \rightarrow Na_2SO_4 + 2HCl$
   **c.** $H_2SO_4 + 2KOH \rightarrow K_2SO_4 + 2H_2O$
   **d.** $2Al + 3CuSO_4 \rightarrow Al_2(SO_4)_3 + 3Cu$

### SECTION 6.1

**1. a.** heterogeneous      **b.** homogeneous
   **c.** homogeneous      **d.** heterogeneous

**2.** Particles in suspension are large and will eventually settle out, so they can be separated by filtering. Particles in a colloid are smaller and do not settle out. Particles in a solution are the smallest. Solutions can be separated by evaporation and distillation.

**3.** In each case, the solution looks uniform and is a uniform mixture of ions, atoms, or molecules that are microscopically undetectable and are spread throughout a single phase.

**4.** The sugar is the solute, or the substance that dissolves in a solution. The water is the solvent, or the substance that dissolves the solute to make a solution.

**5. a.** Liquid fat and water are immiscible, so the less dense fat rose to the top.  **b.** It is a colloid of small pieces of chicken protein spread throughout the water.  **c.** Skim or pour off the layer of fat while the stock is still warm, or cool the stock overnight and lift the solid fat off the surface of the stock.

### SECTION 6.2

**1.** Answers may vary. Possible answers include using warm tap water to dissolve the concentrate, crushing the softened concentrate into smaller pieces, and stirring or shaking the solution.

**2.** You can produce an unsaturated solution by dissolving a small amount of sugar in water. The solution is unsaturated as long as it is able to dissolve more solute. Keep adding sugar until the solution cannot dissolve any more at the given conditions. The solution is saturated if, when you add more solute, it settles to the bottom of the container. Now if you heat the solution, more of the sugar will dissolve, producing a supersaturated solution.

**3.** At the cooler temperature, the solution becomes supersaturated and some of the solute may settle out of the solution to produce a saturated solution under the new conditions.

**4.** 4.0 g acetic acid

**5.** Water is a charged polar molecule. In general, many charged substances (ions and polar molecules) will dissolve in other charged substances. If each substance has a presence of charge, one will likely dissolve in the other.

## SECTION 6.3

**1. a.** acidic  **b.** basic  **c.** neutral  **d.** basic
**e.** neutral  **f.** acidic

**2.** $HNO_3 + H_2O \rightarrow H_3O^+ + NO_3^-$

**3.** $Mg(OH)_2 \rightarrow Mg^{2+} + 2OH^-$

**4.** Strong bases contain hydroxide ions and weak bases react with water to form hydroxide ions. Examples of strong bases include sodium hydroxide, potassium hydroxide, magnesium hydroxide, and calcium hydroxide. Examples of weak bases include ammonia, methylamine, and pyridine.

**5.** The solution with a pH of 3 is $10^3$, or 1000, times more acidic than the solution with a pH of 6. The solution with a pH of 2 is 10 times more acidic than the solution with a pH of 3 and $10^4$, or 10 000, times more acidic than the solution with a pH of 6.

**6.** $2HNO_3 + Mg(OH)_2 \rightarrow Mg(NO_3)_2 + 2H_2O$

## SECTION 6.4

**1. a.** base  **b.** base  **c.** acid  **d.** base  **e.** acid
**f.** base  **g.** acid  **h.** base

**2.** The negatively charged end of soap dissolves in water, while the uncharged end dissolves in oil. This causes the droplets of oil to stay suspended in water and to be rinsed off.

**3.** The long hydrocarbon chains would dissolve in the oil but would not dissolve in water, so the substance would not be able to mix the water and oil throughout one another.

**4. a.** It kills harmful bacteria or viruses.
**b.** 5.8 g $H_2O_2$
(194 g $H_2O$)(3.0 g $H_2O_2$)/(100 g $H_2O$)=
5.8 g $H_2O_2$
**c.** It removes the color from stains by oxidizing the compound responsible.

**5.** The polar end of the methanol molecule dissolves in water, and the nonpolar end dissolves in gasoline, thus removing the water from the tank by carrying it through the fuel system.

## CHAPTER 6 MIXED REVIEW

**1. a.** Check students' drawings for accuracy; see scale in Section 6.3.  **b.** Any liquid with a pH greater than 7 is on the basic side of the scale (in order of increasing pH: egg, sea water, milk of magnesia); any liquid with a pH less than 7 is on the acidic side of the scale (in order of decreasing pH: cow's milk, black tea, orange juice, vinegar). Water is neutral, so it should be at the middle of the scale.
**c.** Orange juice is $10^3$, or 1000, times more acidic than cow's milk. Orange juice is $10^2$, or 100, times more acidic than black tea.

**2. a.** lead nitrate, about 52 g/100 g water; potassium bromide, about 63 g/100 g water; aluminum sulfate, about 105 g/100 g water; potassium iodide, about 143 g/100g water
**b.** The graph of each solid slopes upward, indicating that solubility increases as solvent temperature increases.

**3.** Because toluene doesn't dissolve in charged substances (like polar water molecules and LiCl ions) it must be a nonpolar substance that has an absence of charge.

**4. a.** solutions  **b.** solvent  **c.** heterogeneous
**d.** colloids  **e.** emulsion

# Chapter 7
## Nuclear Changes
### PRETEST

**1.** d

**2.** b

**3.** a

**4.** d

**5.** b

**6.** c

**7.** Mass number is the sum of the protons and neutrons inside the nucleus. Atomic mass refers to the quantity of matter contained in an atom.

### SECTION 7.1

**1. a.** C  **b.** D  **c.** A  **d.** B

**2.** 33 hours. If three-fourths decays, then one-fourth remains unchanged. After the first half-life, one-half of the sample is not changed. After the second half-life, one-fourth is unchanged. The amount of time is equal to $2 \times 16.5 = 33$ hours.

**3. a.** $^{214}_{83}Bi$, beta
**b.** $^{214}_{84}Po$, beta
**c.** $^{210}_{82}Pb$, alpha

4. The neutrons inside the nucleus decay into a proton and an electron. The electron is then ejected during beta-decay.

5. 10 days. One-sixteenth of the original substance will remain after 4 half-lives. This means 40 days is equal to 4 half-lives. So, one half-life is equal to 40 days/4 = 10 days.

6. d

7. a

## SECTION 7.2

1. a. C  b. A  c. B

2. Nuclear fission is started when a fissionable substance is bombarded by neutrons.

3. Answers may vary. Two possible answers are (1) an essential characteristic for a chain-reaction to sustain itself is that the fissionable substance consists of critical mass, and (2) each fission reaction should produce plenty of neutrons to trigger additional fission reactions.

4. Answers may vary. The answer should include that the value of c is very big, making $c^2$ even bigger. Hence, when you multiply a very large number by a small mass, the value of the energy equivalent to that mass is still immense.

5. a. F  b. T  c. T  d. T  e. T

## SECTION 7.3

1. f

2. a. T  b. T  c. F

3. Without proper ventilation, the concentration of radon in the house or school will get dangerously high.

4. alpha and beta rays

5. Ionization occurs when electrons are removed from neutral atoms or molecules. Alpha and beta rays are both capable of ionizing matter.

6. Answers may vary. Excessive exposure to nuclear radiation can damage and change the structure of DNA. DNA holds the genetic information required to build all the proteins necessary for various body functions. So, DNA damage can create serious problems in the manufacture of necessary proteins and in cell function. DNA damage can cause birth defects and illnesses such as cancer.

## CHAPTER 7 MIXED REVIEW

1. a. 1 half-life  b. 3 half-lives
c. 2 half-lives  d. 4 half-lives

2. a. $^{47}_{20}Ca$, beta  b. $^{235}_{92}U$, alpha
c. $^{231}_{90}Th$, alpha  d. $^{40}_{19}K$, beta
e. $^{234}_{90}Th$, alpha  f. $^{14}_{7}N$, beta

3. Check students' graphs. The points to be plotted correspond to successive half-lives, as shown on the x-axis. The corresponding y-values are 1, 1/2, 1/4, 1/8, and 1/16. Answers will vary. Roughly three-eighths or a little less than three-eighths of the sample remains unchanged.

4. 2.70 days. 40 g/160 g = 1/4; one-fourth of the sample remains unchanged after 5.39 days. This implies that 2 half-lives = 5.39 days. Hence, 1 half-life = 5.39 days/2 = 2.70 days

5. Nuclear fusion reactions take place inside the sun, combining light nuclei, primarily hydrogen nuclei, to produce heavier nuclei, and releasing a large amount of energy. Nuclear fusion requires extremely high temperatures. Nuclear fission reactions in nuclear power plants split heavier nuclei into two or more smaller nuclei, releasing neutrons and energy. A critical mass of the fissionable substance is bombarded by neutrons to start the reaction.

6. Answers may vary. Nuclear radiation damages DNA, cells, and tissues. This damage prevents them from functioning properly. Damage to the body on these different levels can cause many serious problems, including birth defects, a decrease in the number of white blood cells, hair loss, sterility, destruction of bone tissue, and cancer. Also, radiation can burn skin and other tissues.

7. a. unstable  b. alpha particles  c. gamma rays  d. beta particles  e. atomic number  f. stable

# Chapter 8
## Motion and Forces
### PRETEST

1. c

2. a, b, d, e, h

3. a, d

4. f

5. b

6. b, c, e, f

7. b

8. d

9. c

## SECTION 8.1

1. The velocity has changed because the car's direction has changed.

2. Answers will vary. To measure time using an analog clock, you measure the rate at which angular distance, or circular distance, is covered by the minute and second hands of the clock.

3. To calculate the distance covered, you measure the total time the car has traveled using the watch. You must also note the speed shown on the speedometer. If the car is traveling at a constant velocity, then the distance covered is equal to $v \times t$.

4. Trains have enormous mass, so even a slow-moving train has a large momentum. A bullet has a very small mass, but when it moves at a very high speed, it has a large momentum.

5. All three objects have equal momentum.
$p = mv = (500 \text{ kg})(64 \text{ km/h}) = (250 \text{ kg})(128 \text{ km/h}) = (1000 \text{ kg})(32 \text{ km/h}) = 3.2 \times 10^4 \text{ kg} \cdot \text{km/h}$

6. If we assume that the car's mass is not changing, then a car that is moving with a constant momentum is traveling at a constant velocity.

## SECTION 8.2

1. $3 \text{ m/s}^2$
$a = \Delta v / \Delta t = (15 \text{ m/s})/5 \text{ s} = 3 \text{ m/s}^2$

2. **a.** Yes **b.** Yes **c.** No **d.** Yes

3. Placing wheels under a heavy box reduces the friction between the box and the ground, making it easier to push the box along at a constant speed.

4. **a.** unbalanced      **b.** unbalanced
   **c.** unbalanced      **d.** balanced

5. **a.** Under the force of gravity, the car will roll down the hill. It will accelerate as it rolls down the hill. **b.** The upward force on the skydiver due to air resistance increases, while the downward force due to gravity stays the same, so the skydiver slows down. **c.** The boat will move at the same constant speed, but its velocity will change because its direction of travel will change.

## SECTION 8.3

1. **a.** third **b.** first **c.** second **d.** second

2. $2.6 \times 10^{-1} \text{ m/s}^2$
$a = F/m = (21 \text{ N})/(82 \text{ kg}) = 2.6 \times 10^{-1} \text{ m/s}^2$

3. Gravitational force depends on the distance between two objects. Because Earth's radius is very large compared with a few hundred meters, the gravitational force—and therefore free-fall acceleration—within a few hundred meters from Earth differs only very slightly from that on Earth's surface.

4. From Newton's first law, we know that an object will move in a straight line at a constant speed as long as no force is acting on it. Since the object is moving in a circular path, there must be a force acting on it. From Newton's second law, we know that if a force is acting on an object it will produce an acceleration that is equal to $F/m$.

5. When two billiard balls that have the same speed collide, they exert forces on each other that are equal and opposite, so the two billiard balls will move in the opposite direction without a change in their speeds.

## CHAPTER 8 MIXED REVIEW

1. **a.** ball A travels 0 m horizontally, ball B travels 30.0 m horizontally, ball C travels 60.0 m horizontally **b.** ball A: 0 m/s,
ball B: $2.0 \times 10^1$ m/s
$v = d/t = (30.0 \text{ m})/(1.5 \text{ s}) = 20 \text{ m/s}$,
ball C: $4.0 \times 10^1$ m/s
$v = d/t = (60.0 \text{ m})/(1.5 \text{ s}) = 40 \text{ m/s}$

2. **a.** 19.5 m/s along the highway
$v = d/t = (3210 \text{ m})/(165 \text{ s}) = 19.5 \text{ m/s}$
**b.** $-2.93 \text{ m/s}^2$
$a = \Delta v / \Delta t = (15.7 \text{ m/s} - 22.0 \text{ m/s})/(2.15 \text{ s}) = -2.93 \text{ m/s}^2$
**c.** $1.98 \times 10^4 \text{ kg} \cdot \text{m/s}$
$p = mv = (1260 \text{ kg})(15.7 \text{ m/s}) = 1.98 \times 10^4 \text{ kg} \cdot \text{m/s}$
**d.** $-3.69 \times 10^3 \text{ N}$
$F = ma = (1260 \text{ kg})(-2.93 \text{ m/s}^2) = -3.69 \times 10^3 \text{ N}$
**e.** 225 s
$t = d/v = (3540 \text{ m})/(15.7 \text{ m/s}) = 225 \text{ s}$

3. The acceleration of both balls is the same, $g = 9.8 \text{ m/s}^2$. The unbalanced force acting on the 5 kg ball is greater, 5 times the unbalanced force acting on the 1 kg ball.

4. Although the object does not experience the force of gravity and is "weightless," it still has mass/inertia and therefore resists any change in its motion.

5. Pulling a heavy object against the force of friction may require more force than lifting the object against the force of gravity.

6. **a.** (free-fall) acceleration  **b.** mass
   **c.** gravity  **d.** air resistance
   **e.** friction  **f.** terminal velocity

# Chapter 9
## Work and Energy
### PRETEST

1. Speed describes how fast an object moves—how much distance is traveled in a given period of time by the object. Velocity is the speed at which and direction in which an object travels.

2. d

3. Its acceleration would also triple.

4. d

5. **a.** the object accelerates  **b.** the object accelerates in the direction of the greater force  **c.** the object maintains its state of motion, whether it is at rest or traveling with a constant velocity

6. the mass of the object and the value of the free-fall acceleration at the location of the object

7. A baseball traveling at 15 m/s has more momentum and more energy than a golf ball traveling at 15 m/s.

8. A baseball traveling at 16 m/s has more momentum and more energy than a baseball traveling at 4 m/s.

### SECTION 9.1

1. **a.** Work is a quantity that measures the effects of a force acting over a distance. $W = F \times d$  **b.** Power is a quantity that measures the rate at which work is done. $P = W/t$  **c.** Mechanical advantage *(MA)* is a quantity that measures how much a machine multiplies force or distance.
   *MA = output force/input force*
      *= input distance/output distance*

2. Power is the rate at which work is done. Power equals the amount of work done per unit time: $P = W/t$.

3. Machines make work easier by allowing you to apply less force at any given moment.

4. $1.8 \times 10^2$ J
   $W = Fd = (120 \text{ N})(1.5 \text{ m}) = 180 \text{ J}$

5. 5.6 kW
   $P = W/t = (250\,000 \text{ J})/(45 \text{ s}) = 5.6 \times 10^3 \text{ J/s}$
      $= 5.6 \text{ kW}$

6. 4.0
   $$MA = \frac{input\ distance}{output\ distance} = \frac{(4.8 \text{ m})}{(1.2 \text{ m})} = 4.0$$

### SECTION 9.2

1. Answers will vary. Sample answers:
   **a.** crowbar  **b.** ax head  **c.** pulley on a flagpole  **d.** car tire, steering wheel  **e.** wheelchair ramp  **f.** machine screw, jar lid

2. Check students' drawings. Labels should show input force, output force, and fulcrum. Use **Figure 9-5** for comparison.

3. A wedge and a screw are both modified inclined planes. A wedge functions like two inclined planes back to back. A screw is an inclined plane wrapped around a cylinder.

4. An inclined plane turns a small input force into a large output force by spreading the work out over a large distance.

5. A wheelbarrow is a second-class lever, and it has a wheel-and-axle on which it moves.

### SECTION 9.3

1. **a.** Kinetic energy is the energy of a moving object due to its motion.  **b.** Potential energy is stored energy resulting from the relative positions of objects in a system.  **c.** Mechanical energy is the sum of the kinetic and potential energy of large-scale objects in a system.

2. $4.2 \times 10^4$ J; $PE = mgh =$
   $(95 \text{ kg})(9.8 \text{ m/s}^2)(45 \text{ m}) = 4.2 \times 10^4 \text{ J}$

3. $4.5 \times 10^3$ J; $KE = (1/2)mv^2 =$
   $(1/2)(74 \text{ kg})(11 \text{ m/s})^2 = 4.5 \times 10^3 \text{ J}$

4. A stretched bungee cord contains elastic potential energy.

5. In the process of photosynthesis, energy from sunlight is captured by plants and stored in sugars and other organic molecules. The energy is stored in the molecules as chemical energy, which is a form of potential energy.

6. The kinetic energy of an object quadruples when the speed of the object doubles.

7. Mechanical energy is the sum of potential and kinetic energy on a large scale, while chemical energy is not measured on a large scale and has little effect on large-scale systems. Chemical energy is the energy stored in the bonds of a chemical compound.

### SECTION 9.4

1. Efficiency is a quantity that measures the ratio of useful work output to work input.

2. Mechanical energy can be transformed into nonmechanical energy due to friction or air resistance, which causes an increase in temperature in the system or in the surrounding environment. Mechanical energy can also be transformed into nonmechanical energy when a sound is produced by friction or an impact.

3. **a.** 60%
   efficiency = useful work output/work input = (45 N)/(75 N) = 0.60 = 60%
   **b.** 87%
   efficiency = (39 N)/(45 N) = 0.87 = 87%
   **c.** 44%
   efficiency = (75 N)(2.5 m)/(425 J) = (187.5 J)/(425 J) = 0.44 = 44%

4. A machine with a high efficiency will transfer a greater amount of the work input to useful work output.

5. With each bounce, some of the ball's mechanical energy is transformed into nonmechanical energy. With less total mechanical energy, the ball cannot bounce as high.

6. At the top of the hill, a skier has mostly potential energy. As the skier glides down the hill, that energy is transformed into kinetic energy, and the skier gains speed. A small amount of the energy may be transformed into nonmechanical energy, which may cause the snow to melt or produce a swooshing sound.

## Chapter 9 Mixed Review

1. **a.** An inclined plane turns a small input force into a large output force by spreading the work out over a large distance. However, because the input distance is longer, the total work done is still the same (or even greater if you take friction into account).
   **b.** In a second class lever, a small force is applied through a large distance. The lever transfers the work to a large force acting through a small distance.

2. **a.** $5.8 \times 10^3$ J
   $PE = mgh = (95 \text{ kg})(9.8 \text{ m/s}^2)(6.2 \text{ m}) = 5.8 \times 10^3$ J
   **b.** 48 W
   $P = W/t = 5.8 \times 10^3 \text{ J}/120 \text{ s} = 48$ W
   **c.** 3.8
   $MA = \dfrac{input\ distance}{output\ distance} = \dfrac{7.5 \text{ m}}{2.0 \text{ m}} = 3.8$
   **d.** $4.8 \times 10^3$ J
   $work\ input = \dfrac{work\ output}{efficiency} = \dfrac{1590 \text{ J}}{0.33} =$
   $4.8 \times 10^3$ J

3. **a.** 58 J
   $KE = (1/2)mv^2 = (1/2)(29 \text{ kg})(2.0 \text{ m/s})^2 = 58$ J
   **b.** 58 J
   $PE$ (at top of swing) = $KE$ (at bottom of swing) by conservation of energy
   **c.** 0.20 m
   $h = \dfrac{PE}{mg} = \dfrac{58 \text{ J}}{(29 \text{ kg})(9.8 \text{ m/s}^2)} = 0.20$ m

4. All machines are less than 100 percent efficient because some energy in a system is always lost to forces such as friction or air resistance. However, this energy does not disappear, it just changes form. Likewise, a machine cannot do more output work than the work that is put into it; that would be creating energy (and would make the machine more than 100 percent efficient).

5. The position of greatest gravitational potential energy and least kinetic energy is when the ball is at its highest point. The position of greatest kinetic energy and least gravitational potential energy is when the ball is at the lowest point in the diagram, right when it hits the floor.

6. **a.** compound machines **b.** lever family **c.** inclined plane or screw **d.** pulley **e.** screw or inclined plane

# Chapter 10
## Heat and Temperature
### Pretest

1. Joules, J

2. a

3. c

4. Answers will vary. Metals, such as copper, iron, steel, aluminum

5. Answers will vary. Materials such as ceramics, wood, air

6. d

7. c

8. The 5 g sample will have the higher temperature.

### Section 10.1

1. Temperature is the measure of average kinetic energy of all the particles in an object. The higher the average kinetic energy, the higher the temperature.

2. The total kinetic energy is the sum of all the kinetic energies for each gas particle in the box. The average kinetic energy is the total kinetic energy divided by the total number of gas particles in the box.

3. As temperature increases, the liquid in a thermometer gains kinetic energy and expands. As the liquid expands, it rises in the tube indicating a higher temperature. As the temperature decreases, the liquid in the thermometer loses kinetic energy and contracts.

4. **a.** 61°F; $T_F = 9T_C/5 + 32 = 9(16)/5 + 32 = 61°F$
   **b.** 35°C;
   $T_C = 5/9(T_F - 32) = 5/9(95 - 32) = 35°C$
   **c.** 243 K; $T = T_C + 273.15 = -30 + 273.15 = 243$ K
   **d.** −173°C; $T_C = T - 273.15 = -173°C$

5. The temperature of the block of iron will decrease and the temperature of the water will increase.

6. The headline is not realistic. Absolute zero (0 K) is the lowest temperature theoretically possible. At absolute zero, all molecular motion stops.

7. The metal will expand when the weather gets hot and the door may get stuck in the frame.

## SECTION 10.2

1. Ceramic is an insulator and does not conduct heat. Stainless steel is a conductor of heat so it will conduct heat away from the oatmeal.

2. Radiation—because they are not touching, energy transfer by conduction cannot occur and because they are in a vacuum, energy transfer by convection cannot occur.

3. **a.** $6.27 \times 10^6$ J; energy = (specific heat) × (mass) × (temperature change) = (4180 J/kg·K) × 100 kg × (15 K) = $6.27 \times 10^6$ J
   **b.** $2.80 \times 10^6$ J; energy = (specific heat) × (mass) × (temperature change) = (1870 J/kg·K) × 100 kg × (15 K) = $2.80 \times 10^6$ J

4. The particles in a gas are more spread out than the particles in a liquid and have less attractive forces acting between them, so if the same amount of energy is transferred to a gas as to a liquid the kinetic energy of the particles in a gas will increase more than the kinetic energy of particles in a liquid.

5. Convection—movement of the hot water as it expands and rises, then cools and contracts, mixes the hot and cold water.

6. Students should defend their answers. A heavy cast iron skillet transfers heat evenly, resists temperature changes, and is slow to heat. A thin stainless steel skillet transfers heat quickly, has a high surface temperature directly over the flame, and cools quickly.

## SECTION 10.3

1. A damp towel has water that absorbs heat energy and evaporates as the air blows through it. Because the air loses heat energy to the water, the air is cooler.

2. **a.** No, the refrigerator releases heat from inside the box out the back of the unit. The refrigerator is in the room, so the heat is still released in the kitchen. **b.** Yes, because shivering causes muscle movements that generate heat **c.** Yes, because the large ears of a jackrabbit act as radiators to radiate heat from the rabbit's blood **d.** Yes, because windows have a low insulating value and large windows would lose large amounts of heat

3. The two objects that will be at different temperatures, such as an inside wall and an outside wall, should be separated by an air-filled space so that they are not touching in order to eliminate heat loss by conduction.

## CHAPTER 10 MIXED REVIEW

1. The metal is a much better conductor of heat than the wood or plastic. Because heat is conducted away from your finger faster, the metal feels cooler.

2. **a.** Warm air causes water to evaporate. The heat lost to the water results in cooler air.
   **b.** In an area with low humidity, more water can evaporate which increases the cooling effect.

3. Heat rises, so to keep heat in the house, the roof needs to be more heavily insulated.

4. Blowing the air out at the top of the room and taking it out near the floor cause the air in the room to mix. If all the vents and returns were either at the ceiling or floor, air in the room would not mix and instead would be in warm and cool layers.

5. Water is the best choice because it has a higher heat capacity than ethanol.

6. **a.** thermometer    **b.** temperature
   **c.** kinetic energy    **d.** zero

# Chapter 11
## Waves
### PRETEST

**1.** b

**2.** Waves will travel faster through liquids because the particles in liquids are much closer together than the particles in gases.

**3.** 2.5 m/s
$v = d/t = 15$ m/6.0 s = 2.5 m/s

**4.** a

**5.** Potential energy is the energy of a system due to the relative positions of the parts of the system. Kinetic energy is the energy of an object in motion due to its motion. There may be potential energy in a system whether the objects are moving or still, but there is kinetic energy only if an object is moving.

**6.** A pendulum has maximum gravitational potential energy when it is at the highest point in its swing. As it swings downward through an arc, some of the potential energy is converted to kinetic energy. At the bottom of the swing, the pendulum has maximum kinetic energy, equal to the initial gravitational potential energy (ignoring air resistance). This process reverses on the upward swing of the pendulum. Energy changes form throughout the pendulum swing, but the total amount of energy stays the same.

### SECTION 11.1

**1.** sound waves—the air; seismic waves—the earth; water waves—the ocean

**2. a.** electromagnetic waves **b.** electric fields and magnetic fields

**3. a.** particles in the medium oscillate perpendicular to the direction the wave travels **b.** particles in the medium oscillate parallel to the direction the wave travels

**4.** Particles in a medium oscillate, or vibrate back and forth, as a wave passes by. The motion of a particle in a medium is like the harmonic motion of a mass vibrating on a spring.

**5. a.** Wave front A would have the largest height, wave front B would have an intermediate height, and wave front C would have the smallest height. A > B > C **b.** wave front C **c.** Each wave front has the same total amount of energy.

### SECTION 11.2

**1. a.** amplitude **b.** trough
**c.** period **d.** frequency
**e.** crest **f.** wavelength

**2. a.** gamma rays **b.** radio waves
**c.** radio waves

**3.** As a source of sound moves toward a person, frequency and pitch increase, wavelength decreases, and wave speed stays the same. As a source of sound moves away from a person, wavelength increases, frequency and pitch decrease and wave speed stays the same.

**4. a.** $f = 2$ Hz, $T = 0.5$ s
$f = 2$ cycles/s = 2 Hz
$T = 1/f = 1/(2$ Hz$) = 0.5$ s
**b.** 0.5 m
$\lambda = v/f = (1$ m/s$)/(2$ Hz$) = 0.5$ m

### SECTION 11.3

**1. a.** The waves would bounce, or reflect, off the surface or boundary. Example: light reflecting off a mirror **b.** The waves would bend, or diffract, as they passed the edge or opening. Example: hearing voices outside the doorway of a classroom (sound waves diffract around the doorway) **c.** The waves would bend, or refract, as they passed from one medium to another (unless they met the boundary straight on). Example: a spoon in a glass of water that looks divided in two (light waves from the spoon inside the water are bent when they pass from water into glass, then into air) **d.** The waves would interfere, or be added or subtracted, as they passed through one another. Example: ripples overlapping on the surface of a pond, producing interference patterns.

**2.** Check students' drawings. Waves that interfere constructively should have crests and troughs lined up with each other, and the resulting wave should be larger than either of the original waves. Waves that interfere destructively should not have crests and troughs lined up, and the resulting wave should be smaller than the larger of the original waves. Use **Figure 11-20** as a reference.

**3.** 1.0 m
$$\lambda = 1 \text{ wavelength} \left( \frac{1.5 \text{ m}}{1.5 \text{ wavelength}} \right) = 1.0 \text{ m}$$

### CHAPTER 11 MIXED REVIEW

**1. a.** D **b.** C **c.** B **d.** D **e.** B, C

**2. a.** A loud sound would be produced at points B and F, where constructive interference occurs. **b.** A softer sound would be produced at points A, C, D, and E, where destructive interference occurs. **c.** Overall, one would hear a series of loud and soft sounds, called beats.

3. Because the moon has no atmosphere, there is no medium on the moon for sound waves to pass through.

4. **a.** one wavelength
   **b.** $f = 3$ Hz, T = 0.3 s, $v = 15$ m/s, $\lambda = 5$ m
   $f = 3$ cycles/s $= 3$ Hz
   $T = 1/f = 1/(3 \text{ Hz}) = 0.3$ s
   $\lambda = v/f = (15 \text{ m/s})/3 \text{ Hz} = 5$ m

5. Interference is a property of all waves. Waves in the same place can combine to produce a single wave that has characteristics that depend on the characteristics of the original waves.

6. **a.** amplitude       **b.** wave speed
   **c.** wavelength      **d.** crest
   **e.** period

# Chapter 12
## Sound and Light
### PRETEST

1. **a.** T **b.** F **c.** F **d.** T **e.** T **f.** F **g.** T **h.** T **i.** F

2. c

3. Check students' drawings for accuracy. Use **Figures 11-9** and **11-10** for reference. The transverse wave should approximate a sine wave; the longitudinal wave should show alternating areas of higher density and of lower density. The wavelength on each type of wave should mark the distance between two successive identical parts of the wave. On the transverse wave, make sure the amplitude marks only half the vertical distance from crest to trough. Amplitude cannot be indicated directly on the longitudinal wave.

4. The frequency of a wave can be determined by counting the number of wavelengths that go past a point in a certain amount of time. The frequency in Hz is equal to the number of cycles (full wavelengths) divided by the time in seconds.

5. d

### SECTION 12.1

1. The speed of sound depends on how often the particles of the medium collide with one another. At higher temperatures, the particles move faster and collide more often.

2. The loudness of a sound depends on the energy contained in the sound waves, which is determined by their amplitude. It also depends on the listener's distance from the source of the sound.

3. The pitch produced by a stringed instrument can be changed by increasing or decreasing the length of the string by moving your fingers to a new position. A shorter length of string vibrates at a higher frequency (pitch), and a longer length of string vibrates at a lower frequency (pitch).

4. The sound from a guitar contains more harmonics than the sound from a tuning fork. A tuning fork vibrates only at its fundamental frequency. A guitar string vibrates at its fundamental frequency and at particular whole-number multiples of that frequency.

5. Sound waves in the air vibrate the eardrum. These vibrations pass from the eardrum to the bones of the middle ear—the hammer, anvil, and stirrup. The stirrup strikes a membrane at the opening of the inner ear, producing longitudinal waves in the cochlear fluid.

6. **a.** 3850 m
   $d = vt = (1540 \text{ m/s})(2.50 \text{ s}) = 3850$ m
   **b.** 1920 m
   $d = (3850 \text{ m})/2 = 1920$ m
   (the depth of the water is half the distance traveled by the sound pulse)

### SECTION 12.2

1. Light can be modeled either as a wave or as a stream of particles. Depending on the situation, light seems to behave either like a wave or like a particle.

2. **a.** wave model       **b.** particle model
   **c.** particle model

3. **a.** radio waves       **b.** gamma rays
   **c.** gamma rays       **d.** radio waves

4. The photons emitted by a bright light bulb and a dim light bulb of the same color have the same energy (but there are more photons emitted per unit time by the bright light bulb). A blue (higher frequency) light bulb emits higher energy electromagnetic waves than a red (lower frequency) light bulb.

5. radio waves, microwaves, infrared light, visible light, ultraviolet light, X rays, gamma rays

6. X rays are used to produce images of bones and other structures. Gamma rays can be used to treat cancer by killing diseased cells.

## SECTION 12.3

1. Light rays striking a rough surface are reflected in many directions, while parallel light rays striking a smooth surface are all reflected in the same direction. Rough surfaces cause diffuse reflection because light rays are reflected in many directions when they hit the uneven surface (the normal to the surface is not always pointing in the same direction).

2. Check students' drawings for accuracy. Use **Figure 12-20** for reference. The angle of incidence and the angle of reflection should appear to be roughly 30°, measured from the normal (perpendicular). The light rays should show directional arrows, and the angle of incidence should lie on the side of the normal where light rays are approaching.

3. Answers may vary. **a.** virtual, stretched **b.** real or virtual, compressed

4. Check students' drawings for accuracy. Use **Figure 12-21B** for reference.

5. **a.** yellow **b.** yellow **c.** black, because blue light contains no yellow light

## SECTION 12.4

1. **a.** toward the normal
   **b.** away from the normal

2. You see a mirage when light is refracted by hot air just above the ground. Your brain may interpret the image of the sky coming from the direction of the ground as a reflection from a pool of water.

3. Total internal reflection occurs when light is completely reflected at a boundary between two transparent mediums because the angle of incidence exceeds the critical angle. Light rays are internally reflected in fiber optic cables, allowing light signals to be transmitted.

4. converging lens—incoming light rays are bent inward by a converging lens

5. **a.** refracts light **b.** acts like the shutter on a camera to allow light to pass through to the lens **c.** refracts light onto the retina at the back of the eye

6. White light is made up of light of different colors. Because light of different colors travels at different speeds in a medium, a prism refracts each color through a different angle. As a result, white light is spread out, or dispersed, into a spectrum of colors.

## CHAPTER 12 MIXED REVIEW

1. Light travels faster than sound. As a result, you see the effects of the gun firing (the smoke) a short time before you hear the gunfire.

2. red light

3. 1 Hz, or one per second

4. **a.** 5s
   $t = d/v = 5$ m/1 m/s = 5 s
   **b.** 2 m/s
   $v = d/t = 10$ m/5 s = 2 m/s
   $d = 10$ m because the virtual image is as far behind the mirror as the object is in front of the mirror

5. Photons from the dimly lit blue light bulb are more energetic than photons from the brightly lit red light bulb because blue light has a higher frequency than red light. The energy of electromagnetic radiation is proportional to the frequency of the radiation.

6. Because the fish is submerged, the fish's eyes are underwater, so the fish should aim below where the insect seems to be. This is because light refracts toward the normal when it passes from the air to water, so the insect appears to be further above the fish than it actually is.

7. Ultrasound can be used to image soft tissues because high frequency ultrasound waves can be reflected from soft tissues when they pass from one type of material into another. The reflected sound waves from different boundary surfaces are compiled by a computer into a sonogram. X rays are very high energy electromagnetic waves and are able to pass through the soft tissues of the body. Some of the X rays are absorbed by the bones. The X rays that pass through the soft tissues to a photographic plate produce a negative image of the hard tissues.

8. **a.** ear          **b.** outer
   **c.** inner        **d.** cochlea
   **e.** ear canal    **f.** stirrup
   **g.** basilar membrane

## Chapter 13
### Electricity
#### PRETEST

1. An atom is made up of protons (positively charged particles), neutrons (neutral particles), and electrons (negatively charged particles). The protons and neutrons make up the dense nucleus of the atom. Electrons are the outermost particles.

2. **a.** F **b.** T **c.** F

3. b

4. c

5. When you touch the doorknob you might feel a small shock.

6. e

7. A ball has gravitational potential energy when it is at the top of a hill. As it rolls down the hill, its gravitational potential energy is converted into kinetic energy. At the bottom of the hill it has only kinetic energy. The total amount of energy of the ball is the same throughout its path (neglecting friction).

8. Possible answers include flashlight, smoke detector, laptop computer, doorbell, calculator, and garage door opener.

## Section 13.1

1. Two unlike charges are attracted to each other.

2. The force is four times greater, or quadrupled. Alternatively, the difference in the forces is equal to three times the original force.

3. **a.** conductor      **b.** conductor
   **c.** insulator      **d.** conductor
   **e.** insulator      **f.** conductor

4. Both charges are positive; the charge on the left is greater.

5. **a.** upward **b.** downward **c.** The electron will have a greater acceleration because it is less massive than the proton.

## Section 13.2

1. There must be a potential difference between the ends of the wire.

2. When an electric device is connected across the terminals of a battery, there is a potential difference across the device and electric charges are accelerated by the electric field in the device.

3. Electric current is the rate at which electric charges move through a conductor. The units of current are coulombs (amount of charge) per second, or amperes.

4. Resistance is due to internal friction slowing the movement of electrons through a conducting material. Resistance can be determined from the ratio of the voltage across a conductor to the current in the conductor using the relationship $R = V/I$.

5. 32 V
   $V = IR = (2 \text{ A})(16 \text{ ohms}) = 32 \text{ V}$

6. $1.8 \times 10^{-2}$ A
   $I = V/R = 12 \text{ V}/650 \ \Omega = 0.018 \text{ A}$

7. Superconductors are materials that have zero resistance when at or below their critical temperature. Conductors are materials in which electric charges can easily be transferred. Insulators are materials in which electric charges are not easily transferred. Semiconductors are between insulators and conductors in their electrical properties.

## Section 13.3

1. battery (1); switch (2); resistors (5) (two are light bulbs)

2. The 20-amp fuse would give greater protection because it would melt at a lower value of current.

3. In a series circuit, there is only one path for electric charge. So current is the same everywhere throughout a series circuit. The voltage across each device in a series circuit may be different. In a parallel circuit, there is more than one conducting path. The voltage across each device is the same, but the current in each device can be different.

4. 53 W
   $P = IV = (2.2 \text{ A})(24 \text{ V}) = 53 \text{ W}$

5. 0.33 A
   $I = P/V = (4.0 \text{ W})/(12 \text{ V}) = 0.33 \text{ A}$

6. $3.1 \times 10^2 \ \Omega$
   $R = P/I^2 = (45 \text{ W})/(0.38 \text{ A})^2 = 310 \ \Omega$

7. Answers may vary. They are connected in parallel, so they have the same voltage across them; therefore, the resistance of each appliance determines the current in the appliance. Alternatively, if one appliance does not work, the others will still be able to function if they are connected in parallel.

## Chapter 13 Mixed Review

1. 2 electrons in a neutral helium-3 atom, no electrons in a helium-3 ion with a 2+ charge

2. Object A and object C attract each other. A and B have unlike charges. B and C have like charges. So A and C have unlike charges.

3. repulsive, because they have equal amounts of charge of the same type **a.** the electric force is one-ninth the original force **b.** the electric force triples

4. Check drawings for accuracy. The − 3 charge should have 3 times more electric field lines pointing toward it than the +1 charge has pointing away from it.

5. The energy stored in the battery is transformed into useful work in the circuit and heat (because of the resistance of the circuit) but does not disappear.

6. Check students' drawings: current is clockwise, and electrons move counterclockwise through the circuit. **a.** battery, switch, resistor (lightbulb) **b.** 0.5 A; $I = V/R = 6$ V/12 $\Omega$ = 0.5 A **c.** 3 W; $P = IV = (0.5$ A$)(6$ V$) = 3$ W

7. **a.** potential difference (or voltage) **b.** electrical potential energy **c.** voltage (or potential difference) **d.** current **e.** charge **f.** cell

# Chapter 14
## Magnetism
### PRETEST

1. The ions repel each other.

2. The negatively charged object will be attracted to the fixed positively charged object and accelerate toward it. Also, it will have greater electrical potential energy when farther from the positively charged object, and this energy will be converted to kinetic energy as it moves toward the positively charged object.

3. The magnets repel each other.

4. A compass needle points in a certain direction because of the presence of a source of a magnetic field, such as a magnet or Earth's magnetic field.

5. **a.** no **b.** yes **c.** yes **d.** yes **e.** yes **f.** yes **g.** yes **h.** yes

6. **a.** yes **b.** yes **c.** yes (or no) **d.** yes **e.** yes **f.** yes **g.** yes **h.** yes (or no)

7. Charges have electrical potential energy as they leave one terminal of the battery, which is converted to kinetic energy as they move through the circuit to the other terminal. Some of the energy is lost as heat due to the resistance of the circuit. The battery increases the energy of the charges as they move through the battery.

### SECTION 14.1

1. Check drawings for accuracy. Two bar magnets that would attract each other would have their N and S poles near each other. Two bar magnets that would repel each other would have either their N poles or S poles together.

2. 4 north poles, 4 south poles

3. Check drawings for accuracy. Refer to **Figure 14-4.**

4. The strength of the magnetic field is greatest near the pole of a bar magnet and decreases with distance from the pole.

5. You are facing east, because north is on your left.

6. At the north magnetic pole, the compass N pole will point straight down. As you move south, the S pole of the compass will tip forward until the needle is horizontal. It will point almost directly north-south. As you approach the south magnetic pole, the compass S pole will tip forward until it points straight down at the south magnetic pole.

### SECTION 14.2

1. The current is to the left. Electrons move toward the right.

2. In magnetic materials, not all of the magnetic fields due to the electrons cancel. In nonmagnetic materials, the magnetic fields of the electrons cancel each other.

3. **a.** increases **b.** decreases

4. Domains are microscopic regions composed of atoms whose magnetic fields are aligned. When an unmagnetized metal core is inserted in a solenoid, the domains reorient to align with the external magnetic field due to the solenoid, magnetizing the metal core.

5. The direction of the current in the coil changes every half revolution so that the loop will rotate in one direction only. If the current in the coil, and therefore the magnetic field, did not change direction every time the coil makes a half revolution, the coil would just bounce back and forth between the poles until friction caused it to come to rest.

### SECTION 14.3

1. An electric current can be produced in a circuit by a changing magnetic field. This can be accomplished by changing the strength, position, or orientation of an external magnetic field.

2. **a.** increase **b.** decrease **c.** increase

3. A moving charge will not experience a force due to a magnetic field if it moves along or opposite the direction of the field lines. As the angle between the moving charge and the magnetic field increases, the force on the charge increases. The force on a moving charge is at a maximum when the charge moves perpendicular to the magnetic field.

4. As the loop is rotated in the magnetic field, charges in the loop experience a changing force due to the magnetic field. For each half rotation the direction of the magnetic force on the charges changes direction.

5. Electromagnetic waves consist of electric field and magnetic field waves that are perpendicular to each other and to the direction of travel. EM waves can travel through empty space because the changing electric and magnetic fields regenerate each other without the need for a medium.

6. **a.** step-down **b.** step-up **c.** step-down

## CHAPTER 14 MIXED REVIEW

1. Check drawings for accuracy. Refer to **Figure 14-5.**

2. Making a magnet: rubbing a metal object with a magnet, placing a metal object near a strong magnet, building a solenoid or electromagnet. Destroying a magnet: heating or striking with a hammer.

3. Both exert the same force, by Newton's third law.

4. The strength of an electromagnet can be increased by increasing the number of coils in the solenoid, increasing the current in the solenoid, and by using a magnetic core that is more magnetizable.

5. The magnetic domains are aligned in some pieces of iron but not in others.

6. Heating a magnet adds kinetic energy to the atoms in the magnet which jostles the domains out of alignment.

7. Gravitational potential energy of the water is transformed into kinetic energy as it falls and rotates a turbine. The kinetic energy of the rotating turbine is transferred to the coil it rotates. As the coil rotates between the poles of the magnet, generating an electric current, the kinetic energy is converted into electrical energy. Some of the energy at each step is lost due to friction.

8. **a.** electric motors **b.** transformers
   **c.** mechanical energy **d.** electrical energy
   **e.** electromagnetic induction **f.** current
   **g.** magnetic field

# Chapter 15
## Communication Technology
### PRETEST

1. d

2. Pure potassium is very soft and reacts vigorously with water at room temperature and gives off hydrogen gas.

3. b and d

4. **a.** 439 hrs (18.3 days)
   $t = d/v = (3.54 \times 10^6 \text{ m})/(2.24 \text{ m/s}) = 1.58 \times 10^6 \text{ s} = 439 \text{ hrs}$
   **b.** $1.32 \times 10^5 \text{ s}$ (36.7 hours)
   **c.** $1.32 \times 10^4 \text{ s}$ (3.7 hours)
   **d.** $1.2 \times 10^{-2} \text{ s}$

## SECTION 15.1

1. **a.** hand gesture **b.** code

2. electric current, electromagnetic waves

3. b

4. The sound waves cause a membrane inside the microphone to vibrate. This creates an analog signal in the form of a changing electric current.

5. 1—current on, 0—current off

6. Answers will vary. Some common answers include CD, hard-disk drive, and DVD.

## SECTION 15.2

1. d

2. The three different types of phosphors give off the three primary colors: red, green, and blue. The three primary colors are sufficient to produce all the remaining colors.

3. c

4. The radio will not be able to pick up a broadcast from any radio stations.

5. The quality of the image becomes better as the number of scan lines increase.

## SECTION 15.3

1. **a.** AND gate and OR gate **b.** Check students' drawings for accuracy. **c.** The porch light comes on because the temperature sensor comes on. **d.** An OR gate is not a good choice. The owner of the house should use an AND gate to control the porch light. This way the porch light comes on only when both the temperature increases above 75°F and it is dark outside.

2. **a.** RAM **b.** ROM

3. compact discs (CD-ROMs) and digital versatile discs (DVD-ROMs)

4. A modem is a device that codes the output data of your computer and uses it to modulate a carrier wave that is transmitted over telephone lines; it also extracts data from an incoming carrier wave and sends that data to your computer.

## CHAPTER 15 MIXED REVIEW

1. Fiber-optic cables are a better choice because they can carry much more information than wire cables.

**2.** 1 and 0

**3.** Digital signals can be sent more quickly and accurately.

**4. a.** re-program their old software  **b.** They have plenty of memory in which to store complete dates.

**5.** No—geosynchronous orbits are at an altitude of about 22 300 miles.

**6.** The electromagnets guide the electron beams across the screen to recreate the broadcast image.

**7. a.** input   **b.** memory
  **c.** processing   **d.** output
  **e.** microphone   **f.** permanent
  **g.** RAM   **h.** AND

# Chapter 16
## The Universe
### PRETEST

**1.** less dense than Earth—because gases have a lower density than solids

**2.** the masses of the planet and the sun, the distance between the planet and the sun

**3.** In nuclear fusion, nuclei of light atoms join together to make a heavier nucleus; in nuclear fission, the nucleus of a heavier atom splits into two or more lighter nuclei.

**4.** As a source of sound moves toward a person, the observed frequency (and therefore the pitch) increases; as a source of sound moves away from a person, the observed frequency (and therefore the pitch) decreases. This is called the Doppler effect.

**5.** d

**6.** radio waves, microwaves, infrared light, visible light, ultraviolet light, X rays, gamma rays

**7. a.** $1.9 \times 10^8$ s (6.0 years)
  $t = d/v = 5.7 \times 10^{16}$ m$/3.0 \times 10^8$ m/s $=$
  $1.9 \times 10^8$ s
  **b.** $3.4 \times 10^{12}$ s (about 110 000 years)

### SECTION 16.1

**1.** Interstellar matter is the gas and dust that exists in the space between the stars.

**2.** The observation that the spectral lines from almost all galaxies are red-shifted is evidence in support of the big bang theory. The cosmic background radiation at microwave wavelengths is also evidence in support of the big bang theory.

**3.** Scientists know the universe is expanding because they can measure the red shifts in the spectral lines of light from galaxies. Almost every galaxy has a red shift, and the farther the galaxy, the greater the red shift. This implies that every galaxy is moving away from every other galaxy—the universe is expanding.

**4.** spiral, elliptical, irregular

**5.** Check students' drawings of the Milky Way galaxy. Drawings should show at least one of the following features: spiral arms; a flat disk; a central bulge.

**6.** $8.2 \times 10^{16}$ m
  $d = vt = (3.0 \times 10^8$ m/s$)(8.7$ years$)$
  $(3.15576 \times 10^7$ s/year$) = 8.2 \times 10^{16}$ m

**7.** Astronomy is the science of looking into the past because all light from stars and galaxies has taken many, many years to reach Earth. When you see light from a distant star or galaxy, you are seeing that object as it was many years ago.

### SECTION 16.2

**1.** Hydrogen and helium

**2.** One star may appear brighter than another for any of the following reasons: it is actually hotter and brighter than the other star; it is larger than the other star; it is closer to Earth than the other star.

**3.** All stars emit light across a wide range of wavelengths, but the wavelength at which it emits the most light depends on the surface temperature of the star. That wavelength also determines the observed color of the star.

**4.** Stars are driven by nuclear fusion reactions, which release a tremendous amount of energy. This energy slowly works its way out through the layers of a star until it is finally released as starlight.

**5.** The sun formed from a cloud of gas and dust collapsing under its own weight. When the center of the cloud became dense enough, nuclear fusion started in the core, and the sun was born. The sun will continue fusing hydrogen into helium for billions of years. When fusion of hydrogen into helium stops, the sun will become a red giant, fusing helium into carbon and oxygen. When fusion of helium into heavier elements stops, the sun will become a white dwarf and eventually burn out completely.

**6.** The energy produced by nuclear fusion in the core of a star pushes outward, counteracting the force of gravity pulling inward.

7. Nuclear fusion in the cores of stars combines lighter nuclei into heavier nuclei, creating the heavier elements. Most stars spend most of their lives fusing hydrogen into helium. Red giants can create elements as heavy as oxygen, and supergiant stars can create elements as heavy as iron. Elements heavier than iron can only be created in supernovas, the explosions that occur when supergiant stars die.

## SECTION 16.3

1. Mercury, Venus, Earth, Mars, Jupiter, Saturn, Uranus, Neptune, Pluto

2. Check students' drawings. Earth should lie directly on the line between the sun and the moon.

3. The inner planets are relatively small and have solid, rocky surfaces.

4. The outer planets, except for Pluto, are large and have thick, gaseous atmospheres. Pluto is more like the inner planets, with a thin atmosphere and a solid, icy surface.

5. The solar system may have formed from a rotating disk of gas and dust (a nebula). The sun formed from the material in the center, and the planets formed from the material farther out (through accretion).

## CHAPTER 16 MIXED REVIEW

1. No. If Betelgeuse were to explode in a supernova tonight, we would not be able to observe the supernova for another 325 years. That is how long it takes light to travel the 325 light-years from Betelgeuse to Earth.

2. There are three possible endings: the universe will expand forever; the expansion will slow down, and the universe will approach a limit in size; or the expansion will stop and the universe will fall back in on itself in a "big crunch."

3. There are more probably more white dwarfs than black holes, because white dwarfs are the remains of small stars. Black holes are the remains of extremely large stars, which are relatively rare.

4. The core of sun will begin to collapse, the fusion of helium into heavier elements will begin, and the sun will expand into a red giant. Eventually, the core will contract again into a white dwarf and slowly cool off.

5. Black holes cannot be observed directly because no light comes from them. A black hole is so massive that not even light can escape its gravitational pull.

6. Check students' drawings. The moon should be drawn off to the side of the line from Earth to the sun.

7. Spacecraft cannot land on Jupiter because Jupiter does not have a solid surface.

8. If the moon's orbit were completely in the same plane as Earth's orbit around the sun, solar eclipses and lunar eclipses would occur every month.

9. The surface of Venus has extremely high temperature and pressure, and the atmosphere of Venus contains sulfuric acid. These harsh conditions may have caused instruments on the spacecraft to melt, break, corrode, or otherwise malfunction.

10. **a.** superclusters    **b.** galaxies
    **c.** elliptical    **d.** irregular
    **e.** stars    **f.** hydrogen

# Chapter 17
## Planet Earth
### PRETEST

1. c

2. d

3. In a longitudinal wave, the particles of the medium vibrate in a direction parallel to the direction of motion of the wave. In a transverse wave, the particles of the medium vibrate in a direction perpendicular to the direction of motion of the wave.

4. c

5. Streak color is a physical property because it does not depend on the reactivity of the chemicals in the rock. The color of a rock is a physical property.

6. b

7. a

8. a

9. b

## SECTION 17.1

1. **a.** continental crust    **b.** oceanic crust
   **c.** lithosphere or crust    **d.** mantle
   **e.** outer core    **f.** inner core

2. Check students' drawings for accuracy. Divergent plate boundary drawings should show plates moving apart. Convergent plate boundary drawings should show plates moving toward each other. Transform boundary drawings should show plates moving horizontally past each other.

3. **a.** volcanoes, mountains, ocean trenches
   **b.** ocean trenches, volcanoes

**4.** Magnetic bands in the rocks under the Atlantic have alternating polarities, demonstrating that Earth's magnetic field reverses about every 200,000 years. These bands are symmetrical to the Mid-Atlantic ridge with the youngest rocks near the center of the ridge. This indicates that the rocks had changed position after cooling, supporting plate tectonics theory.

## SECTION 17.2

**1. a.** longitudinal seismic waves **b.** transverse seismic waves **c.** seismic waves that move along Earth's surface

**2.** A seismograph has a pendulum with a pen at its tip that touches a piece of paper on a rotating drum. When the ground shakes, the rotating drum vibrates under the pendulum and the vibrations are recorded on the paper.

**3.** As plates shift with respect to each other, their edges experience a great deal of pressure. This stress eventually becomes so great that it breaks rocks along the fault, causing an earthquake.

**4.** Shield volcanoes produce gently sloping mountains from typically mild, recurrent eruptions of lava. Cinder cone volcanoes tend to have short, violent eruptions of ash and chunks of lava and then become dormant, producing hills with steep sides.

**5.** Volcanoes form at divergent plate boundaries because as the plates move apart magma rises to fill the gap. At convergent boundaries, magma rises to the surface from the subducting plate to form volcanoes.

## SECTION 17.3

**1.** naturally occurring, nonliving, with a definite chemical composition that can be expressed with a chemical formula, with a characteristic internal structure

**2. a.** igneous **b.** sedimentary **c.** metamorphic

**3. a.** form from compressed or cemented deposits of sediment, older rocks, and organisms: limestone, conglomerate **b.** form when a rock is subjected to high pressure and heat and undergoes a chemical change: marble, slate

**4.** An igneous rock can break down due to weathering. The weathered particles can be carried away by water and wind and deposited, and eventually cemented together to form a sedimentary rock.

**5.** The oldest fossils are at the bottom of the cliff because those rocks were deposited first. Over time, new rock layers are deposited on top of older rock layers. The youngest fossils are at the top of the cliff in the most recently deposited rocks. Answers may refer to the principle of superposition.

**6.** The absolute age of a rock can be found by determining the ratio of the amount of the product of a radioactive material's decay to the amount of the original radioactive material in the rock. The amount of time that passed since the rock formed can be calculated based on this ratio.

## SECTION 17.4

**1. a.** ice, plants **b.** acid rain, $CO_2$ dissolved in water

**2. a.** erosion $\qquad$ **b.** erosion **c.** physical weathering **d.** erosion

**3.** Physical weathering breaks rocks into smaller pieces without changing the rocks' chemical composition. Chemical weathering breaks rocks down by changing their chemical composition.

**4.** Some carbon dioxide dissolves in rainwater, producing an acidic solution. This acidic rainwater reacts with calcite from the limestone to form calcium bicarbonate. This compound dissolves in the water and is carried away, leaving a void.

**5.** Carbon dioxide from the air dissolves in rainwater, forming acidic rainwater that chemically weathers calcite out of limestone to form caves. Acid rain from pollution can weather and erode metal and rock.

**6.** In weathering, rocks are broken down by either chemical or physical means without being removed. In erosion, rocks and the products of weathering are removed.

1. Check students' drawings for accuracy. Divergent plate boundary drawings should have arrows pointing away from each other at the plate boundary, and may include the following geologic features: volcanoes, mid-ocean ridges, and the following geologic events: earthquakes. Convergent plate boundary drawings should have arrows pointing toward each other at the plate boundary, and may include the following geologic features: mountains, volcanoes, ocean trenches, and the following geologic events: earthquakes. Transform fault boundary drawings should have arrows pointing up on the left of the boundary and down on the right of the boundary along the plate boundary, and may include the following geologic events: earthquakes.

2. Scientists study how waves change speed and direction or even stop as they pass through different parts of Earth. By studying these changes, scientists can infer what types of materials are found in different parts of Earth's interior.

3. The Hawaiian Islands formed over a hot spot under the Pacific Plate. As the plate moved, new volcanoes formed, making a chain of islands that differ in age.

4. Sedimentary rock can be exposed to high heat and pressure and undergo a chemical change without melting. The chemical changes produce new minerals in the rock.

5. The surface of the moon must have been molten at some point in the past. This also implies that the moon probably does not have moving plates.

6. near a plate boundary, because rocks at a plate boundary are more likely to experience very high pressure and temperature

7. Answers may vary. The rate of physical weathering by frost wedging will increase if there is more snow and ice, while physical weathering due to plant growth will increase if conditions are more conducive to plant growth. Chemical weathering will increase if the amount of acid rain producing chemicals in the air increases. Erosion due to liquid water is increased if the rate of precipitation increases. Glacial erosion rates will increase if global temperatures decrease enough to send us into an ice age.

8. Erosion by liquid water in streams and rivers can carve out canyons over time. Glaciers can carve out U-shaped valleys in a mountain range as they advance.

9. **a.** focus        **b.** S waves
   **c.** surface waves   **d.** epicenter
   **e.** longitudinal waves

# Chapter 18
## The Atmosphere
### PRETEST

1. **a.** radiation      **b.** convection
   **c.** conduction     **d.** convection
   **e.** radiation

2. on top of the mountain—because the air is less dense at the top of the mountain, more heat will be lost

3. d

4. The speed of light is much greater than the speed of sound.

5. Oxygen gas and ozone are different compounds, and different compounds have different chemical and physical properties.

### SECTION 18.1

1. Nitrogen (about 78 percent) and oxygen (about 21 percent).

2. Check students' diagrams. Refer to **Figure 18-1**.

3. The increased carbon dioxide might increase plant growth because plants use carbon dioxide in photosynthesis.

4. CFCs react with ozone and convert it to oxygen. With less ozone, the amount of ultraviolet radiation that reaches the Earth's surface increases.

5. In a temperature inversion, cool air becomes trapped beneath warm air. In Los Angeles, a temperature inversion would cause pollutants to be trapped in the cool air, causing heavy smog.

6. The troposphere has its warmest temperatures at the bottom and is cooler closer to the top. The stratosphere is coldest at its base and gets warmer with increasing altitude.

### SECTION 18.2

1. **a.** Evaporation is the process by which water molecules escape from liquid water and rise as gaseous water vapor.
   **b.** Humidity is the quantity of water vapor in the atmosphere.
   **c.** Precipitation is any form of water (rain, snow, sleet, or hail) that falls back to Earth's surface from clouds.

2. Check students' drawings. Refer to **Figure 18-12**.

3. Air moves, in the form of wind, from areas of high pressure to areas of low pressure.

4. Winds in the Northern Hemisphere curve to the right, and winds in the Southern Hemisphere curve to the left.

5. Humidity is the quantity of water vapor in the atmosphere. Relative humidity is a ratio of the quantity of water vapor present in the atmosphere to the maximum quantity of water vapor that can be present at that temperature.

## Section 18.3

1. Go to a storm cellar or basement. If no cellar or basement is available, get under a table away from windows. If you are outside, lie in a ditch or low-lying area, and cover your head with your hands.

2. Check students' drawings. Earth should be tilted on its axis so that the Southern Hemisphere is toward the sun.

3. Weather is a description of what is happening in the atmosphere. Climate is an average of weather over a long period of time.

4. In a thunderstorm, water droplets and ice crystals in thunderclouds build up electrical charges. When the charge in a thundercloud becomes different enough from the charge in another cloud or on Earth's surface, lightning jumps as a big spark to equalize the charge.

5. In a cold front, cold air moves quickly under warm air causing warm air to rise rapidly. In a warm front, cold air is slowly overrun by warm air.

## Chapter 18 Mixed Review

1. In the troposphere, temperature decreases as altitude increases. At an altitude of 6000 m, even in the tropics, temperatures are cold enough for snow to occur.

2. The cold glass surface causes water vapor to cool and condense into water droplets, just as cold air causes water vapor to condense into the water droplets that form clouds.

3. It probably will not rain where you are, because weather in Kansas usually moves from west to east due to the wind patterns (called *westerlies*) at that latitude in the Northern Hemisphere.

4. The ozone layer acts as a shield to protect life on Earth's surface by absorbing much of the sun's ultraviolet radiation that enters the stratosphere.

5. The seasons depend on whether the hemisphere is tilted toward the sun or away from the sun rather than the distance from the sun.

6. Tornado Alley has so many tornadoes because cold, dry air from Canada often collides with warm, moist air from the Gulf of Mexico in this area. The intense thunderstorms that form often spawn tornadoes.

7. When isobars are close together it indicates that there is a strong pressure gradient, which usually produces strong winds.

8. The morning with heavy dew was much more humid and the cool air reached or exceeded the dew point. On the morning with no dew, the dew point was not met.

9. The extra solar energy would ionize more molecules in the ionosphere and disrupt some radio communications.

10. **a.** funnel clouds  **b.** tropical depressions
    **c.** thunderstorms  **d.** tornadoes
    **e.** hurricanes  **f.** lightning

# Chapter 19
## Using Natural Resources
### Pretest

1. advantage: the plastic jug will not react with the milk; disadvantage: the plastic jug will not react with other chemicals in the environment that might make it break down

2. No process is ever 100 percent efficient. Some of the energy will be converted to useful work, but some of the energy will be lost as heat or sound due to friction.

3. d

4. The further away the power is used from where it is generated, the greater the total resistance of the power lines because resistance of a wire increases with length. As resistance increases, the efficiency will decrease because more of the energy will be lost as heat as a result of the internal friction of the wires.

5. carbon dioxide, water

6. oxygen, water

### Section 19.1

1. Answers will vary. The living elements of an ocean reef ecosystem include the coral creatures that build the reef, fish, and any other creatures that live on the reef. Nonliving elements include sunlight, the reef, ocean water, and gases dissolved in the water.

2. The elements that make up an ecosystem function together (are interrelated) to keep the entire system stable, so a change in one feature can affect the whole system.

3. **a.** short          **b.** long
   **c.** long           **d.** short

4. Short-term, long-term

5. Answers may vary. Possible answers include clearing trees, driving cars, and constructing buildings.

6. To evaluate the effects of their decisions on the issues that cause change in their environment, people must first understand how the many parts of an ecosystem relate to one another.

7. Major projects, such as building a dam, must undergo an environmental analysis by engineers before construction begins.

## SECTION 19.2

1. photosynthesis

2. Fossil fuels come from fossilized plant and animal remains that are dug from the ground. solid–coal, liquid–oil, gas–natural gas

3. burning fossil fuels, hydroelectric dams, nuclear power plants

4. **a.** fission and fusion **b.** fission **c.** the disposal of highly radioactive waste

5. **a.** non-renewable, advantage: inexpensive, disadvantage: polluting **b.** renewable, advantage: non-polluting, disadvantage: not efficient in all parts of the world **c.** renewable, advantage: non-polluting, disadvantage: **d.** renewable, advantage: cheap energy, disadvantage: destroys natural environment, only usable for a limited amount of time because dams silt up

6. 1/4

## SECTION 19.3

1. Postal deliveries of the bill are eliminated—so fuel is not consumed (pollutants are not emitted). Paper envelopes used in mailings are eliminated—so the production of paper products (a very costly and polluting industry) is reduced.

2. **a.** The combustion of fossil fuel produces carbon dioxide, a greenhouse gas. The continual buildup of greenhouse gases causes an increase in Earth's temperature.
**b.** Weather patterns could change, bringing droughts to some areas and floods to others. The level of the sea could rise as polar ice melts.

3. It makes water acidic; this can harm or even kill aquatic life. It makes soil even more acidic; this can damage large tracts of forests and harm or kill life in the soil.

4. industrial waste, agricultural fertilizers, and everyday human activities

5. Many land-based pollutants do not dissolve well in water, making them very difficult to remove.

6. reducing use of energy and products (using fabric grocery bags, lowering thermostats), reusing products whenever possible (reusing plastic or paper grocery bags), recycling (aluminum cans, car parts)

## CHAPTER 19 MIXED REVIEW

1. In a balanced ecosystem, there are enough resources for every living thing. The population sizes of the different species do not change relative to one another. The living and nonliving elements are balanced so that the ecosystem is stable and can be maintained over a long period of time.

2. **a.** The cattle grazed upon the grasses, decreasing their dominance; this allowed more mesquite to move into the area.
**b.** The grasses would regain their former dominance.

3. **a.** 3000 times more energy to produce an aluminum can than in the drink that it carries; $1.8 \times 10^6$ J/600 J = 3000 **b.** It is extremely wasteful if we remove aluminum from the ground as bauxite ore, spend a lot of energy and money to process it, and then return it to the ground as landfill. To recycle costs only about half the energy, and reuses a valuable resource.

4. **a.** B **b.** A **c.** C

5. **a.** fossil fuels **b.** renewable **c.** wind **d.** geothermal **e.** nuclear power

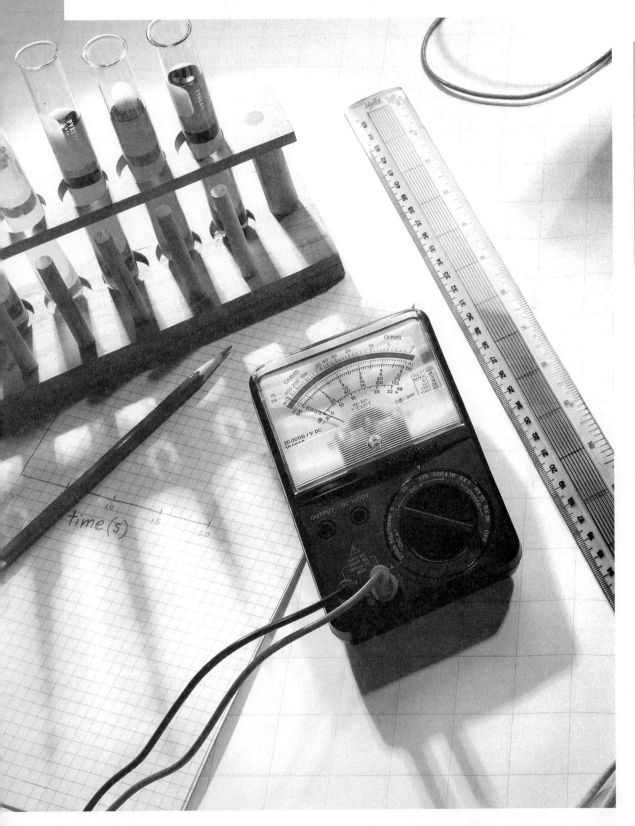

# INTEGRATION WORKSHEETS
# ANSWER KEY

# INTEGRATION WORKSHEETS ANSWER KEY

## WORKSHEET 1.1: Serendipity and Science
### Integrating Biology

1. Student answers will vary, but possible answers include: curiosity, knowledge of bacteria, dedication to research.
2. Student answers will vary, but possible answers include: curiosity, responsibility, medical knowledge, ability to analyze data and draw conclusions.
3. The discovery of the hantavirus depended on science. If the team had not developed the habits, skills, and knowledge of science, they might not have listened or might not have recognized the important information, or known how to follow up on it.

## WORKSHEET 1.2: The Structure of Medical Terminology
### Connection to Language Arts

1. c
2. f
3. g
4. i
5. j
6. e
7. b
8. a
9. h

## WORKSHEET 1.3: The Chemistry Connection
### Integrating Chemistry

1. All living organisms, including humans, contain proteins. Proteins are necessary for life.
2. Humans must get the building materials for proteins from the food they eat.
3. The human body is like a chemistry lab. Matter and energy are constantly being changed by body processes.

## WORKSHEET 1.4: Using Quantitative Statements to Solve Problems
### Integrating Mathematics

1. $v = (450 \text{ km})/(10 \text{ h}) = 45 \text{ km/h}$
2. $d = v\Delta t$
3. $d = v\Delta t = (400 \text{ m/min})(10\text{min}) = 4000 \text{ m}$

4. Answers should contain these ideas: the time a moving object remained in motion is equal to the distance it traveled in that time divided by the average speed.

## WORKSHEET 1.5: Observing and Experimenting to Find Relationships
### Integrating Physics

1. direct
2. inverse
3. Answers should contain these ideas: the amount of pressure at any point in a container of liquid is directly related to the depth that point is below the surface of the liquid.

## WORKSHEET 2.1: What's Special About Indigo?
### Integrating Biology

1. Natural indigo is extracted from a plant while synthetic indigo, which has the same chemical formula, is produced in the laboratory.
2. Indigo could not be produced in the laboratory until its chemical formula was known. This was discovered in 1883, and synthetic indigo was made soon afterwards.
3. Synthetic indigo can be made much more efficiently than natural indigo can be extracted from plants.
4. Indigo dye does not penetrate fibers completely, and it continually fades.

## WORKSHEET 2.2: Is Dry Cleaning Dangerous?
### Science and the Consumer

1. Some dangers associated with limited exposure to perchloroethylene are dizziness, headaches, skin irritation, and loss of consciousness; longer exposures can damage the liver and kidney, and may cause cancer.
2. One advantage to wet cleaning is that the danger of possible exposure to perchloroethylene is eliminated. One disadvantage is that wet cleaning does not work with all materials.

**3.** No; the reading discusses the dangers that result from exposure to perchloroethylene, but does not claim that such exposures necessarily accompany the process of dry cleaning. This is a matter of debate, as can be seen by the clause *"some people fear* that dry cleaning poses a danger to human health".

## WORKSHEET 2.3: Uses of Pumice
### Integrating Earth Science

**1.** Pumice often floats across the ocean for long distances before it becomes waterlogged and sinks to the ocean floor.

**2.** Pumice mines are found in the Rocky Mountain and Pacific Coast states.

**3.** Pumice is used in soaps, cleansers, dental products, polishing and scouring products, poured concrete, insulation, acoustic tile, stucco, and plaster. It is also used to polish and grind television glass and to sculpt stone and ivory.

**4.** abrasiveness

## WORKSHEET 2.4: Our Changing Universe
### Integrating Space Science

**1.** Huge amounts of radiation prevented protons, neutrons, and electrons from binding together immediately after the big bang.

**2.** Light atoms such as hydrogen, hydrogen's isotopes deuterium and tritium, helium, and lithium were the first to form.

**3.** Light elements were formed when protons, neutrons, and electrons from the big bang explosion joined together; heavier elements are formed in nuclear reactions that occur in stars.

**4.** Because stars continue to produce heavier elements in nuclear reactions, the distribution of elements 10 billion years from now will be different than it is today.

## WORKSHEET 2.5: Choosing Materials for Bicycle Frames
### Real World Applications

**1.** weight, cost, resistance to rust, strength, elasticity

**2.** Plastic is light and inexpensive, but it is not strong enough to hold up well in crashes, and as a result is not a good choice for a bicycle frame.

**3.** If a material is not strong enough or too brittle, crashes would be much more dangerous for the rider.

**4.** Titanium would be a better choice, because speed is probably more important than cost for one of the country's top racers.

## WORKSHEET 2.6: Hidden Meanings
### Connection to Language Arts

**1.** Knowing a word's derivation can make it easier to remember the word's current meaning, and can also help you avoid confusions between it and related words. For example, if you know the etymologies of the words element and compound, you will be less likely to confuse these two words.

**2.** No; although this can often be done, it is not always possible. This is because sometimes the word evolves so much that its original meaning no longer applies, as with the word *atom*.

**3.** Answers may vary but should correctly incorporate the etymologies of the two words. Possible answers include: knowing nature, an attempt to know more about nature, a study of nature with the goal of knowledge.

## WORKSHEET 2.7: Plasma
### Integrating Physics

**1.** Plasma is a mixture of positive ions and free electrons; three examples are the interior of stars, neon signs, and the aurora borealis and australis.

**2.** Although we usually observe matter in its solid, liquid, and gaseous forms on Earth, most matter in the rest of the universe, including the interiors of stars (which are much more numerous than planets like Earth), is in the plasma state.

**3.** Plasma is considered to be a fourth state of matter because its properties are very different from the properties of gases. For example, plasmas inside stars can be much more dense than a gas.

## WORKSHEET 2.8: Ozone Depletion
### Integrating Environmental Science

**1.** Ozone is harmful in the lower atmosphere, where it is a form of pollution, but it is helpful in the upper atmosphere, where it filters out harmful ultraviolet radiation from the sun.

**2.** In the upper atmosphere, CFCs release chlorine atoms, which break apart ozone molecules.

**3.** Answers about the importance of complying with the Montreal Protocol will vary. Check for accurate reasoning and agreement with the facts stated in the reading.

# WORKSHEET 3.1: How do Scientists Find Cures for Diseases?
## Real World Applications

1. Answers will vary, but each procedure should limit the results to compounds of molecular structures of Type II or V that inhibit the growth of bacteria B and have minimal side effects.

2. Answers will vary. Be sure students follow the procedure they established in step 1 for each of the six compounds.

3. Compounds #4 and #6 are the most likely candidates for a cure, and should be tested further.

# WORKSHEET 3.2: Buckyball
## Connection to Architecture

1. The buckyball molecule is made up of 60 carbon atoms joined together. The atoms are arranged in a spherical, cage-like structure with a hollow interior, similar to a soccer ball or a geodesic dome.

2. Because buckyballs are perfectly spherical, there are hollow spaces between them which easily can hold other atoms or molecules, thereby creating new materials.

# WORKSHEET 3.3: Magnesium: From Sea Water to Fireworks
## Integrating Earth Science

1. Magnesium alloys are used in the construction of airplanes, racing cars, boats, and various other objects because they are light-weight, like magnesium itself, but stronger than pure magnesium.

2. Racing cars and boats must be relatively light-weight to be able to move quickly.

3. Magnesium works well in fireworks and bright flashlights because it burns with an intense, white flame.

4. A magnesium alloy is a better choice than magnesium because it is stronger than pure magnesium and will not burn as well in air.

# WORKSHEET 3.4: Chemical Symbols
## Connection to Language Arts

1. Copper
2. Iron
3. Tungsten

# WORKSHEET 3.5: Carbon-Dating Masterpieces
## Connection to Fine Arts

1. A living organism is constantly exchanging the carbon in its body with the carbon in the air. The carbon in the air contains a set ratio of carbon-14 to other carbon isotopes. Therefore, the organism has the same ratio of carbon-14 to other carbon isotopes as the air does.

2. When the organism dies, the carbon-14 begins to decay. The organism is no longer exchanging carbon with the air, so the carbon-14 atoms that have decayed are not replaced.

3. If just the number of carbon-14 atoms were considered, it would not be clear how many carbon-14 atoms were in the sample when it was living. If this were not known, it would be impossible to calculate how many atoms had decayed, and carbon-14 dating would not work.

4. No. If the atoms did not decay at a constant rate, it would be impossible to calculate exactly how long the atoms had been decaying.

# WORKSHEET 3.6: The Elements in Your Body
## Integrating Biology

1. Student answers should have any three of the following: water, protein, carbohydrates, lipids, and nucleic acids.

2. It helps keep bones strong and is needed to maintain cellular structure.

3. Trace elements are elements that your body requires in very small amounts. Examples are any two of the following: cobalt, copper, fluorine, silicon, and tin.

4. A well-balanced diet ensures that your body gets all of the different vitamins and minerals it needs to function.

# WORKSHEET 3.7: Seeing Atoms: the STM
## Integrating Technology

1. The Greek theory was not based on experimental evidence, while Dalton's theory was.

2. The STM made it possible to "see" atoms for the first time.

3. An STM samples the distribution of electrons on the surface, and then uses this data to generate a computer image of the atoms on the surface.

## WORKSHEET 3.8: Atomic Fingerprints
### Integrating Physics

1. In the Bohr model, electrons can only be found in certain, discrete energy levels; they are never between levels, but instead "jump" from one level to the next without passing through the intermediate regions.

2. These lines correspond to the "jumps" an electron makes from one energy level to another. There is a finite number of lines, rather than a continuous spectrum, because the electron can only jump from one energy level to another.

3. The pattern of lines is similar to a fingerprint in that each element has its own, unique pattern of lines which can be used to identify the element.

4. A scientist could compare the pattern of lines to the known patterns of each element, and this comparison would reveal what element or elements are contained in the gas.

## WORKSHEET 4.1: What Happens in a Kiln?
### Connection to Fine Arts

1. No, you could not make porcelain in a kiln that only reaches 1000°C because porcelain must be fired to at least 1300°C.

2. Before the clay is fired in a kiln, there are no chemical bonds holding the clay particles together. As a result, water could easily tear the clay particles apart, causing the object to lose its shape.

3. Porcelain is fired to a higher temperature than terra-cotta, so there are more chemical bonds holding the clay particles together. As a result, porcelain is more durable than terra-cotta.

## WORKSHEET 4.2: Linus Pauling: A Life Well Spent
### Connection to Social Studies

1. Pauling feared that the after-effects of nuclear testing, such as birth defects, cancer, and other diseases, would affect generations for years to come. He believed it was a mistake to stockpile large amounts of weapons so powerful that they could completely destroy all of civilization, and he also feared the possibility of a nuclear accident.

2. Student answers will vary, but should express the fact that informed decisions about nuclear weapons cannot be made without a scientific understanding of their effects.

3. Student answers will vary. Whatever side they choose, be sure students explain their opinions with an appropriate argument.

## WORKSHEET 4.3: Ion Propulsion in *Deep Space 1*
### Integrating Space Science

1. When an electron hits a xenon atom, it knocks another electron off the xenon atom, and the xenon atom becomes a positively charged ion.

2. The ion beam and the spacecraft move in opposite directions.

3. No, the ion drive would not work if the xenon atoms were not charged. This is because the neutral xenon atoms would not be accelerated by the electrically charged grids, and as a result there would be nothing to propel the spacecraft forward.

## WORKSHEET 4.4: Plastics
### Integrating Environmental Science

1. They are both polymers.

2. Plastic helps keep food fresher, so it's less likely to spoil. Less spoiled food means less waste.

3. Plastic benefits the environment because it helps prevent waste and improve energy efficiency. Plastic harms the environment because it does not degrade once it is discarded.

## WORKSHEET 4.5: Amino Acid Combinations
### Integrating Mathematics

1. Long chains of amino acids

2. 400

3. 160 000

4. Answers will vary, but should be similar to the following: Determine how many positions there are. Determine how many choices there are for each position. The total number of possible combinations is equal to the number of choices multiplied by itself the same number of times as there are positions.

## WORKSHEET 4.6: Fractions of Crude Oil
### Connection to Engineering

1. Crude oil is separated into batches with different properties. Each one of these batches is called a fraction.

**2.** Diesel fuel is used for heat, so it used more often in the winter months.

**3.** The demand for gasoline might decrease because people do less driving on the whole during winter. Most vacations, for example, take place in the summer. And roads are often more dangerous in the winter, so people may tend to drive less.

# WORKSHEET 5.1: Hot Meals on Hand
## Real World Applications

**1.**

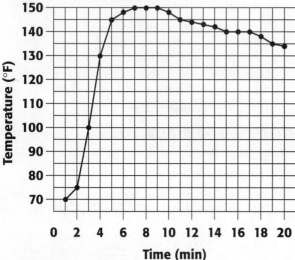

**2.** About 4.5 min

**3.** 15 min (20 min after reaction begins)

# WORKSHEET 5.2: Organisms that Glow
## Integrating Biology

**1.** Because organisms that could emit blue light would be able to attract food and those that emitted other colors could not, blue-light emitting organisms had the best chance to thrive and breed.

**2.** Exothermic, because the bioluminescence reaction emits energy in the form of light.

**3.** Fluorescence relies on a light source that contributes energy that is later re-emitted. Bioluminescence is exothermic.

# WORKSHEET 5.3: Limestone Reactions
## Integrating Earth Science

**1.** From top to bottom: stalactite, stalagmite, column of calcium carbonate.

**2.** $CaCO_3 + H_2CO_3 \rightarrow Ca(HCO_3)_2$

**3.** No. Calcium carbonate crystallizes out of solution, but no new product is formed.

# WORKSHEET 5.4: The Chemistry of Art
## Connection to Fine Arts

**1.** Aluminum and iron should be avoided for the sculpture near the lighthouse because both decay when exposed to salt water.

**2.** Yes. Exposed metal parts of buildings are exposed to the same environmental hazards as outdoor sculpture.

**3.** The sculptor might want the high-polish finish possible with silver and the low cost of making the bulk of the sculpture from lead.

# WORKSHEET 5.5: Fireworks
## Connection to Social Studies

**1.** Red: lithium, Li, or strontium, Sr. White: magnesium, Mg. Blue: copper, Cu.

**2.** Barium, Ba and antimony, Sb

**3.** Fireworks are dangerous because they contain black powder and other chemicals that are highly explosive.

# WORKSHEET 5.6: The Right Fire Extinguisher for the Job
## Science and the Consumer

**1.** Use on A; Don't use on B or C.

**2.** No. Because it does not indicate that it is good for class C, electrical fires, you would not want to use it on your computer.

# WORKSHEET 5.7: Fertilizers: Friend Or Foe?
## Integrating Environmental Science

**1.** Nitrogen

**2.** Farmers can grow healthier plants in less space.

**3.** Fertilizer can contaminate drinking water and food, and help to transform an area into a bog.

**4.** Answers will vary, but could include ideas about reducing the amounts of excess fertilizer in the soil, or ideas about developing new fertilizers that do not have the problems that current fertilizers have, or ideas about increasing land use and paying higher prices so fertilizers will not be as necessary.

# WORKSHEET 5.8: Alchemists' Theory of the Elements
## Connection to Social Studies

**1.** He could taste the powder and taste another sample of seawater. He would find they both tasted salty.

2. The powdery substance left in the bowl was the same color as the water. There was no color change.

3. No. No new substance was formed, the salt was simply separated from the water. There was no color change.

# WORKSHEET 6.1: What Is Your Favorite Flavor?
## Real World Applications

1. Chromatography is a technique used to separate out the parts of a mixture.

2. Chromatography is used to separate out the various compounds that make up certain flavors and fragrances. Once researchers know what compounds a flavor or fragrance is made up of, they can recreate the flavor or fragrance in the laboratory.

3. It is often cheaper to make a compound than to extract it from a plant. Synthetic compounds are also advantageous when the natural supply is limited.

# WORKSHEET 6.2: Detergents: Helpful or Harmful?
## Connection to Social Studies

1. Soaps leave residues in some kinds of water, while detergents do not.

2. Some people fear that high phosphate levels in lakes can cause an overgrowth of algae and weed, which could deplete the lake's oxygen supply.

3. Answers will vary. Check for logical consistency and accurate reasoning, and be sure students' statements agree with the facts presented in the reading.

# WORKSHEET 6.3: The Centrifuge
## Integrating Physics

1. In a suspension, the particles settle out over time. In a colloid, the particles do not settle out naturally.

2. No, it would not. The separation of solids in a suspension is due to the force of gravity acting upon them.

3. If the axis of rotation is near the top of the container, the denser particles will move away from it toward the bottom of the container.

# WORKSHEET 6.4: A Balance In The Body
## Integrating Biology

1. A buffer maintains the pH level when small amounts of acids or bases are added to the system.

2. Acids, which contain hydronium ions, decrease the pH. Bases, which contain basic ions, increase the pH.

3. Both buffering reactions have two products: water, and the opposite buffering agent.

# WORKSHEET 6.5: Phospholipids
## Integrating Biology

1. Both molecules have one portion that attracts water and one portion that repels water.

2. The cell's contents would dissolve in the watery environment.

3. If the cell membrane could not interact with water it would not be able to move necessary substances into and out of the cell. If it could not repel water then the cell would dissolve.

# WORKSHEET 7.1: Radioactivity Within the Earth
## Integrating Earth Science

1. Heat is given off because of radioactive decay within Earth.

2. Answers will vary, but students' responses should be similar to the following: A fluid heated in one area expands, becoming less dense. Because the heated fluid is less dense, it is displaced by the cooler, more dense fluid surrounding it, and it rises.

3. The high temperature and pressure make the mantle able to flow.

# WORKSHEET 7.2: The Life Cycle of a Star
## Integrating Space Science

1. hydrogen

2. Some of the mass is converted to energy.

3. Only extremely massive stars produce the enormous gravitational forces needed to create iron through fusion.

# WORKSHEET 7.3: Radiation and Medicine
## Real World Applications

1. Interventional radiology

2. You can take X rays to find out if the arm is really broken.

3. Radiotherapy

# WORKSHEET 7.4: Nuclear Powered Space Probes
## Integrating Space Science

1. The radioisotope provides energy in the form of heat as it decays.

**2.** Current is in the circuit because one of the materials produces a voltage when it is at a higher temperature.

**3.** Radioisotopes work well in remote locations, such as outer space or the deep ocean, where solar energy or fossil fuels are impractical.

## WORKSHEET 7.5: A Remarkable Discovery
### Connection to Social Studies

1. 5370 years
2. More than half
3. 1600 atoms
4. 26850 years

## WORKSHEET 7.6: Marie Curie and the Naming of a Unit
### Connection to Language Arts

**1.** Marie and Pierre discovered polonium and radium.

**2.** A curie is a unit of radioactivity equal to the amount of a radioactive nuclide that decays at $3.7 \times 10^{10}$ disintegrations per second.

**3.** Before she went to the university, Marie was a teacher and a governess.

**4.** No. Most women of her time were not involved in scientific careers.

## WORKSHEET 7.7: Radiochemistry
### Integrating Chemistry

**1.** Radiochemists further our understanding of chemical processes using the properties of radioactive isotopes.

**2.** This happens in neutron activation analysis.

**3.** Chemical reactions can be analyzed by converting one of the reactants into a radioactive isotope before the reaction takes place. After the reaction has occurred, the product can be measured for radioactivity to determine how much of the given reactant is present.

## WORKSHEET 7.8: Environmental Radiation
### Integrating Environmental Science

**1.** The three most common sources of natural background radiation are cosmic rays, radiation from elements in the earth, and radiation from organisms.

**2.** Living organisms release radiation by taking in trace radioactive elements which then decay in their bodies.

**3.** Radiation can come from Earth's surface or may be released into air.

**4.** Two radioactive isotopes found in living organisms are carbon-14 and potassium-40.

## WORKSHEET 8.1: An Expanding City
### Connection to Social Studies

**1.** $v = d/t = \dfrac{16.3 \text{ km}}{19 \text{ min}} \times \dfrac{60 \text{ min}}{\text{h}} = 51 \text{ km/h}$

**2.** $d = vt = (5.0 \text{ km/h})(19 \text{ min})(\text{h}/60 \text{ min}) =$
$$1.6 \text{ km}$$

**3.** Accept all reasonable answers. For example: cars are cheaper and easier to produce now so more homes have at least one car, leading to congested roads and increased travel times.

## WORKSHEET 8.2: Hiking in Yellowstone
### Real World Applications

**1.** (2.5 mi)(1 h/3 mi) + (350 ft)(1 h/2000 ft) =
$$0.83 \text{ h} + 0.175 \text{ h} = 1.0 \text{ h}$$

**2.** (5.5 mi)(1 h/3 mi) + (3400 ft)(1 h/2000 ft) =
$$1.8 \text{ h} + 1.7 \text{ h} = 3.5 \text{ h}$$

**3.** (2 mi)(1 h/3 mi) + (1300 ft)(1 h/2000 ft) =
$$0.66 \text{ hr} + 0.65 \text{ hr} = 1.3 \text{ h}$$

## WORKSHEET 8.3: Jesse Owens in the 100 Meter Dash
### Integrating Mathematics

**1.**

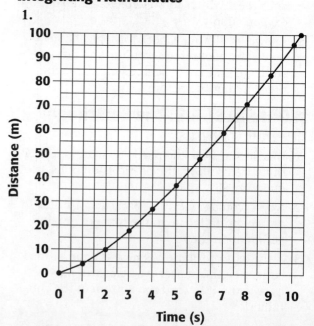

**2.** The graph has the steepest slope between 10.0 s and 10.3 s. Accept all reasonable answers for where the graph appears to have the steepest slope. The slope of the graph is steepest where the speed of the runner is greatest.

**3.**

| Time (s) | Total distance (m) | Average speed (m/s) |
|---|---|---|
| 1.0 | 4 | 4 |
| 2.0 | 10 | 6 |
| 3.0 | 18 | 8 |
| 4.0 | 27 | 9 |
| 5.0 | 37 | 10 |
| 6.0 | 48 | 11 |
| 7.0 | 59 | 11 |
| 8.0 | 71 | 12 |
| 9.0 | 83 | 12 |
| 10.0 | 96 | 13 |
| 10.3 | 100 | 13.3 |

## WORKSHEET 8.4: Car Seat Safety
### Science and the Consumer

1. Children are safer in the back seat of a car because many air bags in the front were designed for adults and may not be as safe for children.

2. Up to 80% of car seats are not used or installed correctly. A federal law requiring "a simple, universal system for attaching car safety seats" would help to ensure that all car seats are installed and used correctly so that they can function to protect children in car accidents.

3. The safest place for a child safety seat is in the center of the back seat, because this position would be furthest from any side-impact collision.

## WORKSHEET 8.5: Gravity and the Planets
### Integrating Space Science

1. The object would reach the ground first on Earth, second on Mars, and last on the moon because gravitational acceleration is the greatest on Earth and the least on the moon.

2. The gravitational force is the least on the moon, so Monique will be able to jump the highest.

3. Ellis will land on the trampoline first because the force of gravity on him (due to Earth) is the greatest. Not only will he be falling from a lower height, but his acceleration will be greater.

## WORKSHEET 8.6: How Fish Maintain Neutral Buoyancy
### Integrating Biology

1. Buoyancy is an object's ability to float.

2. Accept all reasonable answers. Buoyant: a leaf, any boat, a life vest, most people. Not buoyant: a steel nail, a rock, a brick.

3. Neutral buoyancy is when an object remains suspended in water because it displaces a mass of water equal to its own mass.

4. Its swim bladder enables the goldfish to achieve neutral buoyancy. Gases from nearby blood vessels diffuse into and out of the small lined swim bladder sac as needed to maintain neutral buoyancy.

## WORKSHEET 8.7: Momentum of Line in Art
### Connection to Fine Arts

1. A

2. D

3. Lines that are thick or bold, have no obstacles on the top surface, are straight or have a gentle transition into a curve.

4. Scientists use the term to describe the tendency of a speeding car to go straight when it come to a sharp curve. Artists use the term to describe the tendency of the eye to go straight when it comes to a sharp curve after moving quickly along a straight line.

## WORKSHEET 8.8: Hydraulic Lift Force
### Integrating Technology

1. 50 N

2. 1000 times as large

3. 6 N

## WORKSHEET 8.9: Energy Costs of Running and Walking
**Integrating Health**

1.

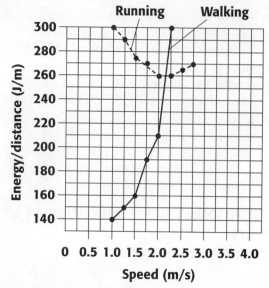

2. **a.** running **b.** running **c.** walking
3. About 2.25 m/s. The body will naturally adapt to the motion that requires the least energy.

## WORKSHEET 9.1: Muscles and Work
**Integrating Biology**

1. Anaerobic exercise
2. Aerobic exercise is best for the heart and lungs because they get exercise by providing the muscles with oxygen.
3. **a.** doing a running long jump: anaerobic
   **b.** running the 100 m dash: anaerobic
   **c.** running a marathon: aerobic **d.** doing push-ups: resistance

## WORKSHEET 9.2: The Pyramids
**Connection to Social Studies**

1. The Egyptians used levers and inclined planes, or ramps to move stone blocks up to the top of the pyramids.
2. $(2.2 \times 10^4 \text{ N}) \times (2 \text{ m}) = 4.4 \times 10^4 \text{ J}$
3. $d = W/F = (9.0 \times 10^5 \text{ J})/(4.5 \times 10^4 \text{ N}) = 2.0 \times 10^1 \text{ m}$

## WORKSHEET 9.3: Calories and Nutrition
**Real World Applications**

1. $4.39 \times 10^5 \text{ J}$
2. 263 Calories, or $1.10 \times 10^6 \text{ J}$
3. Answers will vary, but students should have the minimum number of foods from each food group, and the total Calorie count should be between 2000 and 3000.

## WORKSHEET 9.4: Batteries and Emerging Technology
**Integrating Technology**

1. A battery converts chemical energy into electrical energy.
2. Rechargeable batteries are useful for alternative-fuel cars because operating them does not cause any pollution and they can easily and repeatedly store energy from other sources.
3. The engines must rely on more than one source of energy because each energy source has drawbacks. The gasoline-powered engines create pollution, and the battery-powered engines cannot produce enough energy to power the car for long periods of time.

## WORKSHEET 9.5: The Concept of Energy
**Connection To Language Arts**

1. Rene Descartes
2. Thomas Young
3. Galileo developed the concept of work. This began the development of the concept of energy because one definition of energy is the capacity to do work.
4. The vis viva is equal to twice the kinetic energy of an object.

## WORKSHEET 9.6: Chemical Reactions
**Integrating Chemistry**

1. Energy is the ability to do work.
2. Hand warmers do not create energy. Instead, they release the energy that they had previously stored.
3. Chemical energy is a form of potential energy because chemical energy is the result of the position of objects in a system: it is the result of the position of the atoms in the substance.

## WORKSHEET 9.7: Understanding the Conservation of Energy
**Integrating Environmental Science**

1. The law of conservation of energy is the principle of physics that states that energy in a closed system is neither lost or created.
2. Usually they are referring to new ways to capture and convert energy that is already around us.
3. The law of conservation of energy ensures that energy is not created or destroyed, but it does not stop us from converting usable energy into energy that is harder to use.

# WORKSHEET 10.1: Starlight, Star Heat
## Integrating Space Science

1. Longer wavelengths are associated with cooler temperatures.
2. The sun belongs to spectral class G.
3. Red stars have longer wavelengths and cooler temperatures than blue stars have. Red is long and cool. Blue is short and hot.

# WORKSHEET 10.2: Skin Temperature
## Integrating Health

1. Student charts should include the following zones: 15°C—no sensation; 32°C—cold; 33°C–34°C—comfort; 35°C–39°C—warm to hot; 39°C–41°C—pain; 41°C–44°C—burning pain; 45°C+—rapid tissue damage
2. A warm or hot sensation is expected above 37°C.
3. 32°C
4. Skin temperature varies much more than core temperature.

# WORKSHEET 10.3: Land and Sea Breezes
## Integrating Earth Science

1. The sun is the source of the energy transferred to the sea and the land.
2. Water warms up more slowly than land, so water has a higher specific heat value. A substance with a higher specific heat requires more energy to raise its temperature than substances with a lower specific heat require.
3. Students should use arrows and labels to indicate warm air rising over the ocean and cool air moving from the land to the ocean.

# WORKSHEET 10.4: Early Central Heating
## Connection to Social Studies

1. hypocaust: convection; fireplace with wall: radiation; French system: convection; steam heat: conduction and convection
2. hypocaust, French system
3. A fireplace and an electric space heater are similar because both heat by radiation.

# WORKSHEET 10.5: Hibernation and Torpor
## Integrating Biology

Student tables should be in the following order: Shrew, Hummingbird, Honey possum, Marmot, Bear.

1. Bear; Bear
2. Shrew; Shrew
3. The larger the body mass, the longer the cool-down and warm-up times.
4. Animals take longer to cool down than to warm up.

# WORKSHEET 10.6: Appliance Energy Use and Cost
## Real World Applications

1. $\dfrac{\dfrac{24.3 \text{ kWh}}{1 \text{ month}}}{\dfrac{4 \text{ h}}{1 \text{ d}} \times \dfrac{30 \text{ d}}{1 \text{ month}}} = 0.20 \text{ kWh/h for TV}$

$\dfrac{\dfrac{2 \text{ kWh}}{1 \text{ month}}}{\dfrac{2 \text{ h}}{1 \text{ d}} \times \dfrac{30 \text{ d}}{1 \text{ month}}} = 0.03 \text{ kWh/h for VCR}$

The difference is 0.17 kWh/h.

2. $\dfrac{6 \text{ kWh}}{1 \text{ month}} \times \dfrac{2 \text{ h}}{0.5 \text{ h}} \times \dfrac{8.5 \text{ cents}}{1 \text{ kWh}} = \$2.04/\text{month}$

3. $\dfrac{153.6 \text{ kWh}}{1 \text{ month}} \times \dfrac{9.9 \text{ cents}}{1 \text{ kWh}} = \$15.21/\text{month}$

4. Answers may vary. Sample answers are given. Drying takes more electrical energy, but this figure does not include the cost of water and heating the water.

# WORKSHEET 10.7: The Little Ice Age
## Connection to Social Studies

1. Glacial polishing is the smoothing of smoothing of rock due to the force of a glacier moving over it.
2. The temperature decreased by approximately 1-2°C.
3. Tide records show that sea level dropped during that period. There is also evidence of glacial advance during those years.
4. The changed weather conditions led to crop failures, famine, and an increase in disease.

# WORKSHEET 10.8: Thermal Pollution
## Integrating Environmental Science

Answers will vary. Tables should be logically arranged and include places to record at least the following items: Date, distance of test site from point of waste water entry, temperature of water, and evaluation score.

## WORKSHEET 11.1: Wave Energy
### Connection to Engineering

1. transverse waves
2. An electric generator is attached to the propeller of an OWC.
3. Passing waves move the buoy up and down, moving an arm attached to the piston.

## WORKSHEET 11.2: Bicycle Design and Shock Absorption
### Science and the Consumer

1. The seat and the handlebar-frame connection are areas in which the rider comes in direct contact with the bicycle.
2. Another good place for shock absorbers is where the wheels attach to the frame and at various joints in the frame.
3. Helmets are shock absorbers. They absorb some of the energy that results from the head hitting a hard surface, such as the street, in an accident.

## WORKSHEET 11.3: Earthquake Waves
### Integrating Earth Science

1. **a.** Love wave  **b.** P-wave  **c.** Rayleigh wave  **d.** S-wave
2. Body waves take a more direct route through Earth instead of around its surface.
3. Surface waves cause the most damage because they disturb the surface of Earth.

## WORKSHEET 11.4: Architectural Acoustics
### Connection to Architecture

1. Sound travels the slowest in air.
2. Cork is the best choice for controlling sound reflection. The texture of cork provides plenty of holes filled with air to trap and slow sound waves.

## WORKSHEET 11.5: Radio Waves
### Integrating Technology

1. Electrons vibrating in an antenna produce radio waves.
2. Answers will vary. Examples are: toasters produce infrared electromagnetic waves, microwave ovens produce microwaves, light bulbs produce mostly visible light and infrared radiation.
3. The radio signal is lost because the electromagnetic waves are absorbed by the rocks and soil of the tunnel.

## WORKSHEET 11.6: Writing a Plan for Wave Observation
### Connection to Language Arts

Answers should be consistent with the stated objective. For example,

**Objective:** to observe wave frequency

**Instruments Used:** stopwatch or clock

**Observing Process:** Count the number of crests or troughs that pass some object, such as a post on a pier, in a certain amount of time.

**Data Record:** table of crests that passed a point and the time interval

## WORKSHEET 11.7: Bending Light Waves to Magnify
### Integrating Mathematics

1. $5\times$
2. 500% larger than the size of the actual object
3. $\frac{3}{4}''$ original + $3\text{-}\frac{3}{4}''$ increase = $4\text{-}\frac{1}{2}''$ magnified image

## WORKSHEET 12.1: How Does Sunscreen Work?
### Real World Applications

1. Sunburns occur when ultraviolet radiation causes the expansion of small vessels in the skin that contain red and white blood cells. Suntans occur when melanin is released to the outer surface of the skin as a protection against ultraviolet radiation.
2. The pigments in sunscreen and melanin both serve the same function: absorbing ultraviolet radiation so that it does not penetrate the skin.
3. 20 SPF sunscreen absorbs 19/20 of the UV rays, allowing only 1/20 to penetrate the skin.
4. Without any sunscreen, people with higher levels of melanin will tan more easily, while people with less melanin will tend to burn because their bodies have less protection against the sun's ultraviolet radiation.

## WORKSHEET 12.2: The Refracting Telescope at Yerkes
### Integrating Space Science

1. The 40-inch telescope at Yerkes is the largest refracting telescope in the world.
2. A movable floor is necessary because the telescope pivots around the middle of its tube; as one end is moved to observe different parts of the sky, the other end (which contains the eyepiece) also moves. As a result, the eyepiece is not always at the same height.

3. Stars move so slowly that smaller time periods do not reveal their motion.

## WORKSHEET 13.1: Incandescent Light Bulbs
### Connection to Social Studies

1. Halogen bulbs last longer because they continually rebuild the filament.
2. Tungsten atoms evaporate because the filament is so hot.
3. No. You would be manipulating two variables: type of bulb and wattage.

## WORKSHEET 13.2: Electric Eels
### Integrating Biology

1. Yes. The longer the eel, the more electroplaques it would contain in its body. Similar to batteries, the more electroplaques, the more power.
2. Normal voltage is either 110 or 220. Electric eels can discharge about 5 times 110 or about 2.5 times 220.
3. Yes. An electric eel can discharge enough electricity to stun or possibly kill a human. River water is a good conductor of electricity. If the eel discharges enough electricity, the current could travel through the water and shock the person.

## WORKSHEET 13.3: Battery Issues
### Science and the Consumer

1. Rechargeable batteries are more economical because they last longer.
2. Answers may vary. Sample answer: Rechargeable, because less of them are needed.
3. Answers may vary. Sample answer: Call the local waste management office to get instructions on disposing of batteries.

## WORKSHEET 13.4: Electric Shock: Caution!
### Real World Applications

1. No. The bird is not affected because it is not touching the ground. The children are touching the ground, so picking up the line would give them an electric shock.
2. The ground wire provides a path for electricity—other than through the person using the tool—in case the tool malfunctions.
3. No. The metal dryer is a good conductor. If the wire is in contact with the dryer, the dryer will be part of the circuit and will be charged. If you touch the door, you can act as a path to ground for the current.

## WORKSHEET 13.5: Rechargeable Ni-Cd Batteries
### Integrating Chemistry

1. Battery power is more useful when an appliance needs to be portable.
2. The electrons come from the cadmium anode.
3. Because regular batteries can be used only once, they must replaced when worn out. Rechargeable batteries cost only pennies to recharge, so replacing single-use batteries is more expensive in the long run.
4. Students' answers should be logical and supported by details. For example: Rechargeable batteries are less harmful to the environment than regular batteries because they can be recharged by electricity from renewable sources. Because they can be used many times, they do not contribute as much toxic materials to landfills as single-use batteries do.

## WORKSHEET 13.6: Recording Electricity in the Brain
### Integrating Health

1. EEG stands for electroencephalogram.
2. Brain waves show less intense activity when you relax.
3. During an epileptic seizure, brain waves show more intense activity.
4. Neurons send electrical signals using chemicals.

## WORKSHEET 14.1: The Natural Forces and Laws of Compasses
### Connection to Social Studies

1. The gyroscopic compass is more susceptible to mechanical failure because it has moving parts.
2. Yes, a gyrocompass is an example of Newton's first law. A magnetic compass is not.
3. A ship with a gyrocompass might need a magnetic compass to set the gyrocompass to point north.

## WORKSHEET 14.2: Molecular Magnetism
### Integrating Chemistry

1. Watermelon. It is a diamagnetic material because it contains water. The others are not.
2. The magnetic force field created by the magnet isn't strong enough to overcome the force of gravity pulling the grape down.

3. No. The direction of the magnetic force must be opposite the force of gravity to keep the object aloft.

## WORKSHEET 14.3: Magnetic Resonance Imaging
### Integrating Technology

1. MRI provides a noninvasive view of internal body tissue.

2. a strong magnetic field

3. The signal of the hydrogen atoms as they move back into alignment after being forced out of alignment by radio waves produces the radio waves that result in an image.

4. Because the metal parts might be attracted to the strong magnetic field, MRI instruments cannot be used on people with metal implants.

## WORKSHEET 15.1: Morse Code and Computers
### Connection to Social Studies

1. Morse code was invented for the telegraph.

2. Morse code led to the use of paper tape to convey and store information. Paper tape was used in the first computers.

3. Paper tape transmitters use two rows, one for dashes and one for dots. In Morse code, the dashes took three times as long to deliver as the dots, but with the paper tape, they took the same amount of time. Also, since there were two rows on the paper tape, a dot and a dash could be delivered at the same time instead of one after the other.

## WORKSHEET 15.2: The Brain's Signals
### Integrating Biology

1. The function of neurons is to gather, use, and distribute information.

2. Axons are branches that allow one neuron to connect to others.

3. Receptors in the skin gather information such as texture and temperature.

## WORKSHEET 15.3: High-Definition Digital Television: Why Make the Switch?
### Science and the Consumer

1. The Federal Communications Commission regulates interstate communications.

2. Students should explain two advantages. Possibilities include: more bandwidth will be available for the government to use for other purposes, digital television signals can transmit more information, digital television signals allow the use of new, high-definition television sets, digital television signals will allow viewers to have more programs to choose from.

3. Students should explain two disadvantages. Possibilities include: television stations have to pay to make the changes to their equipment, and consumers will have to buy either a converter or a high-definition television to be able to view the new digital images.

## WORKSHEET 15.4: Building a Computer
### Integrating Physics

1. 69, 141

2. Find one number of millimeters on a ruler. Line up the second ruler so "0" on it matches the first ruler's number, and the second ruler's numbers get bigger closer to "0" on the first ruler. Then move along the second ruler to find the other number. At that point, read the number on the first ruler that matches. This is your answer.

d. 9, 18

## WORKSHEET 15.5: Computers and Design Fields
### Connection to Architecture

1. slide rule

2. Architects can E-mail important messages and design plans to clients instantaneously.

3. A computer simulation can let the designer know if there are any flaws in the design or miscalculations in the plans of the design. A computer simulation can also help designers, or their clients, quickly make decisions about the structure, or even the colors, of their products.

## WORKSHEET 15.6: World Wide Web Robots
### Real World Applications

1. Student answers should name a Web search engine, such as Altavista or Lycos.

2. A Web robot is a computer program that has been designed to search the Web and compile information.

**3.** Answers will vary. Possible answers are: Different search engines might think that their robots are better at finding Web pages to index that people are interested in. Different search engines might be trying to specialize in certain types of information, so they would want their robots to look for certain kinds of web pages.

## WORKSHEET 15.7: Arts and the Internet
### Connection to Fine Arts

**1.** Three art forms being changed by the Internet are creative writing, music, and visual art.

**2.** Answers will vary, but student should mention that Internet art museums allow people to view art that they might not get to see otherwise, because it is so far away. Also, Internet art museums allow viewers to view art at any time, rather than only during museum hours.

**3.** Answers will vary, but student should mention that many unknown bands may want people to hear their music so they can become popular and well-known.

## WORKSHEET 15.8: Converting Binary Numbers
### Integrating Mathematics

**1.** 4, 1, 21

**2.** 11, 10010, 1001101

## WORKSHEET 16.1: Science Fiction and Fact
### Connection to Language Arts

Students' descriptions of life on a space station in 2075 should suggest reasonable technological advances in meeting human needs in space.

## WORKSHEET 16.2: Red Shift, Blue Shift
### Integrating Physics

**1.** Both stars are moving away from Earth. Star A is moving faster than Star B.

**2.** There are several possible conclusions. Accept any one of the following: the spacecraft and the star are moving toward each other; the spacecraft is moving toward the star faster than the star is moving away from the spacecraft; the star is moving toward the spacecraft faster than the spacecraft is moving away from the star; the star is stationary and the spacecraft is moving toward it.

**3.** Because light that appears red is moving away from the observer and light that appears blue is moving toward the observer, one side of the apparent edge of a rotating body will appear blue and the opposite edge will appear red. If the east edge appears blue and the west edge appears red, the body is rotating from east to west.

## WORKSHEET 16.3: Using Comparisons to Understand Space Statistics
### Integrating Mathematics

Answers may vary. Sample answers are given.

**1.** The moon is less than a third the diameter of Earth.

**2.** Mercury is less than half the diameter of Earth.

**3.** Venus is slightly smaller than Earth.

**4.** Mars is about half the diameter of Earth.

**5.** Jupiter is about 11 times the diameter of Earth.

**6.** Saturn is nearly 9.5 times the diameter of Earth.

**7.** Uranus is about 4 times the diameter of Earth.

## WORKSHEET 16.4: Exercise in Space
### Integrating Health

**1.** Astronauts use their upper body muscles to pull themselves around in the weightless environment, so they do not need extra exercise.

**2.** Because the vertical position helps them experience the nerve and muscle patterns normally experienced in Earth's gravity.

**3.** To better mimic the effects of low gravity.

**4.** The LBNP could provide a means of maintaining lower-body muscle tissue even while remaining horizontal, as bedridden people do.

## WORKSHEET 17.1: High Up in the Himalayas
### Integrating Physics

**1.** Just as thin ice cannot support a large weight, a thin crust of 5 km could not support the great weight of the enormous Himalayan mountains. As a result, they would sink down into Earth's crust.

**2.** India continues to move further into Eurasia, exerting an upward force that is slowly increasing the height of Mount Everest.

**3.** India will have moved 2 million cm (1 million years × 2 cm/year), or 20 km.

## WORKSHEET 17.2: Plinian Eruptions
### Connection to Social Studies

**1.** The most minor type of volcanic eruption is characterized by lava flows.

**2.** Gas, ash, and volcanic rock

**3.** The gas and ash in an eruption can cause suffocation.

**4.** Students' discussions of volcanic damage will vary. Two possibilities are damage due to pieces of falling rock, or fire damage sparked by lava flows.

## WORKSHEET 17.3: Human Tools: From Stone to Iron
### Connection to Social Studies

**1.** hardness and brittleness

**2.** Bronze tools were more durable, easier to shape and reshape, and they could be re-sharpened as needed.

**3.** Answers will vary. Be sure students give a plausible relationship an archaeologist 2000 years from now might make between form or material and function for the tool from our time that they have chosen.

## WORKSHEET 17.4: From Granite to Paper
### Integrating Chemistry

**1.** In physical weathering, mechanical agents such as wind and rain break down rocks into smaller parts and transport them to new locations, but the chemical composition of the rocks remains unchanged. In chemical weathering, chemical reactions alter the minerals in rocks, transforming them into new substances.

**2.** Kaolin is a deposit left by the weathering of the minerals in granite. This is a chemical process, because the minerals in granite are actually changed into new substances with different properties, such as kaolin.

**3.** Kaolin's primary use is as a coating for paper.

**4.** Kaolin is Georgia's most important mineral industry. Georgia invests money in the development of new applications to ensure that there will continue to be uses for kaolin in the future, even if current processes that require kaolin (such as paper production) develop in new ways that no longer depend on kaolin.

## WORKSHEET 17.5: The Eruption of Mount Pinatubo
### Integrating Environmental Science

**1.** Two environmental effects of a major volcanic eruption are increased acid rain and cooler temperatures.

**2.** Sulfur dioxide particles from the eruption turn into aerosols in the upper atmosphere. These aerosols block some of the sun's rays, thereby decreasing temperatures.

**3.** Volcanic particles that reach the stratosphere can be spread around the globe by strong winds. As a result, volcanic effects on climate and weather can reach locations that are very far from the eruption.

**4.** NASA researchers were especially interested in Mount Pinatubo because its effects on the atmosphere were much more significant than those of smaller eruptions.

## WORKSHEET 17.6: Living Sources of Weathering
### Integrating Biology

**1.** Some common causes of physical weathering are wind, water, and ice. Some common causes of chemical weathering are carbonic acid and acid rain.

**2.** Digging animals uncover buried rock surfaces and expose them to forms of physical and chemical weathering.

**3.** Plant roots can break apart rocks, and plant acids can break down rocks such as limestone.

**4.** Plant roots break apart rocks by means of a physical force or pressure, so this is an example of physical weathering. Plant acids actually dissolve the cements that hold the rock particles together, so this is an example of chemical weathering.

# WORKSHEET 17.7: Names of Rocks
## Connection to Language Arts

| | Everyday meaning | Earth science meaning (as a rock classification) | Latin root and its meaning |
|---|---|---|---|
| **Igneous** | relating to or characteristic of fire | rocks that are formed from cooled or hardened magma or lava | *ignus:* fire |
| **Sediment/ Sedimentary** | material that settles to the bottom of a liquid or is deposited on an underlying surface | rocks that have formed from compressed or cemented deposits of sediment | *sedimentum:* settling, from *sedere:* sit |
| **Metamorphosis/ Metamorphic** | any kind of change or transformation | rocks that are formed from other rocks through heat, pressure, or chemical processes | *metamorphosis:* change |

# WORKSHEET 17.8: Mountaineering: How Our Bodies Acclimatize
## Integrating Biology

1. Mountain climbers must either carry extra oxygen or acclimatize their bodies because there is less oxygen at high altitudes.

2. During acclimatization, hemoglobin-carrying red blood cells increase in number, and other changes to muscles and blood vessels occur that facilitate oxygen transfer.

3. Human acclimatization is a temporary process in which hemoglobin levels increase. The genetic adaptation of certain mountain animals is permanent, allowing them to receive the necessary amount of oxygen from their normal hemoglobin levels.

# WORKSHEET 18.1: Why Your Ears Pop
## Integrating Health

1. You would develop an earache whenever you changed your altitude because of the pressure.

2. Under water, the pressure outside the eardrum is greater than that inside the eardrum.

3. It would be pressed towards the outside. The greater pressure on the inside would push into the area of lesser pressure, and the eardrum would be pushed out.

# WORKSHEET 18.2: Understanding Thunderstorms
## Real World Applications

1. 49 000°F

2. Because light travels faster than sound, you see lightning before you hear thunder.

3. The lightning is about 1.6 kilometers, or 1 mile, away.

# WORKSHEET 18.3: Adobe
## Integrating Physics

1. Adobe soil is a mixture of clay, sand, and silt.

2. Good heat conductors allow energy to flow very quickly when there is a temperature difference, while good heat insulators do not.

3. Metals are very good heat conductors, so a house with metal walls would not be energy efficient. In the summer the house would warm up too quickly and in the winter it would cool down too quickly.

# WORKSHEET 18.4: The Tropopause
## Integrating Physics

1. The troposphere

2. Answers will vary, but they should contain a description similar to the following: Part of a fluid, such as air or water, is heated. As the fluid is heated, it expands, and decreases in density. Because the heated portion of the fluid is less dense than the unheated portion, the force of gravity causes the heated portion to rise. As it rises, it transfers energy to previously unheated areas.

3. Yes. The water on the bottom of the pan gets warmer and moves to the top of the pan. When the hot water moves up, it carries the heat with it and distributes it throughout the water.

4. The height of the tropopause would rise if average temperatures increased. The height of the tropopause would fall if average temperatures decreased.

## WORKSHEET 18.5: The Layers of the Atmosphere
### Connection To Language Arts

1. The highest layer of the atmosphere is the thermosphere.

2. The name stratosphere is derived from the Latin word "stratus," and the Greek word "sphaira."

3. All the layers of the atmosphere have "sphaira" as their base because each of them is shaped like a ball (or sphere) that surrounds the earth.

## WORKSHEET 18.6: Cloud Seeding
### Integrating Chemistry

1. Three substances commonly used for cloud seeding are sodium chloride (salt crystals), hydrogen chloride, and water sprays.

2. Cloud seeding can be used to try to reduce the number of lightning strikes during a thunderstorm.

3. Students should mention that substances are introduced into the cloud that increase the chance that the water droplets will begin to bind to each other, creating bigger drops and possibly rain.

## WORKSHEET 18.7: Doppler Weather Radar
### Integrating Technology

1. Radar works by sending radio waves out from an antenna. When the waves hit an object, they are deflected back to a receiving antenna, where they are amplified and transformed into an image that illustrates the location of the object.

2. The Doppler effect is an apparent change in the frequency of a wave when the source of the wave is moving in relation to the observer.

3. Doppler weather radar is better for forecasting because it gives forecasters information about the velocity and direction of winds. This information can help forecasters recognize dangerous weather phenomena.

## WORKSHEET 19.1: TVA: Finding Solutions
### Connection to Social Studies

1. It improved farm productivity and supplied new jobs by attracting industries to the area.

2. TVA will mix waste gases from Memphis's wastewater treatment plant with coal to fuel the production of electricity.

3. Memphis will have cleaner air, and TVA will save money on fuel costs.

## WORKSHEET 19.2: Solar Energy
### Science and the Consumer

1. Solar energy can be used to heat water, swimming pools, homes, and offices; to cook; to pump water; and to generate electricity.

2. Solar energy is a renewable resource, and it is pollution free. One disadvantage of solar energy is that it is sometimes more expensive than other energy sources.

3. The amount of available sunlight determines, in part, whether it is feasible to collect enough sunlight to meet energy needs at a reasonable cost.

4. You should weigh the cost of each energy source, the location of your home, and the environmental effects of each option.

## WORKSHEET 19.3: Composting
### Integrating Biology

1. Humus provides nutrients and helps the soil retain moisture.

2. Regular stirring keeps a plentiful supply of air mixed throughout the compost pile; the microorganisms depend on this air for their survival.

3. Compost is free and effective fertilizer, and it keeps organic waste matter from taking up space in landfills or creating pollution in a garbage-burning plant. Manufacturing fertilizers is more expensive and produces chemical byproducts as waste.

## WORKSHEET 19.4: Recycling Plastics
### Science and the Consumer

1. The codes indicate what type of plastic the product is made of.

2. In some cases, a single incorrectly sorted piece of plastic could contaminate an entire bale, making it unable to be recycled.

3. One advantage is that is saves plastics from taking up landfill space; one disadvantage is that it can be costly.

4. Reusing plastic products when possible saves the cost of transporting and processing the plastics that are involved in recycling.

# WORKSHEET 19.5: The Meaning of Efficiency
## Connection to Language Arts

1. Something that is efficient saves time, money, or other resources.

2. In everyday usage, efficiency involves saving money, time, and resources. The same is true with respect to appliances; in this context, efficiency involves saving resources (energy use) and, as a result, saving money for the consumer.

3. Efficient appliances use less energy and cost less to run.

4. The cheapest oven will not necessarily be the best value in the long run, because it might cost much more to operate. To find the best value overall, the consumer must consider both the initial cost and the efficiency of each model.

# WORKSHEET 19.6: Pesticides
## Integrating Chemistry

1. Many farmers rely on pesticides to reduce the damage done to their crops by pests.

2. Pesticides affect many animals other than the pests, such as natural predators of pests, bees, birds, and other wildlife, and they also pollute ground water, well water, streams, and lakes.

3. Accept all reasonable answers that agree with the facts presented in the reading. For example: farmers must be educated on ways to reduce pesticide use and on alternatives to pesticides, and funding must be provided for them to implement new measures. A combination of pesticide reduction and alternative methods could significantly decrease pesticide use in the United States without sacrificing our crops.

# WORKSHEET 19.7: Solar Cells
## Integrating Physics

1. A solar cell is a device that converts sunlight into electricity.

2. No, a solar calculator would not work in a dark room because it is powered by the energy from light; without this energy, there would be no electricity to power the calculator.

3. No; how well an array of solar cells works depends on how much sunlight the cells receive, and this varies in different locations.

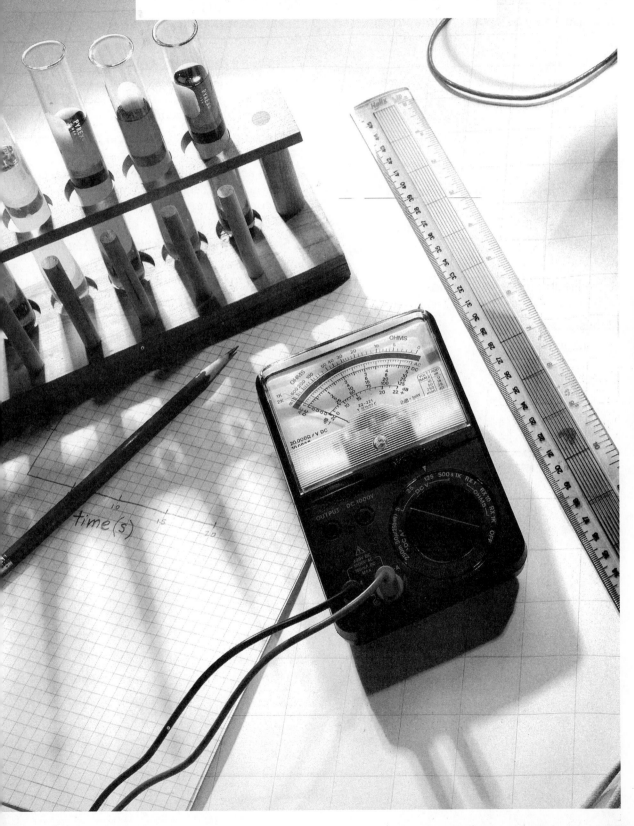

# BASIC SKILLS
# ANSWER KEY

BASIC SKILLS

# BASIC SKILLS WORKSHEETS ANSWER KEY

## 1.1 Understanding Symbols

**1.** 440 kg•m/s²    **2.** 3.0 cm/s    **3.** 38 cm

## 1.2 Basic Exercises in Logic

### 1. Constructing a Diagram for the Premises

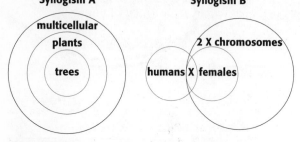

Syllogism A                    Syllogism B

### 2. Using the Diagram to Determine the Conclusion

Syllogism A: All trees are multicellular.

Syllogism B: Some humans have two X chromosomes.

### 3. Evaluating Other Conclusions

1. cannot determine
2. false
3. cannot determine

## 1.3 Creating A Concept Map

### 1. Determining the Main Concepts

Student answers will vary. Possible answers include organize ideas, outline, concept map, main ideas, boxes, lines, letters and numbers, show relationships, graphic, easy to remember.

### 2. Choosing the Central Concept

Student answers may vary. Be sure a central concept is chosen. Possible answers include concept map, organize ideas.

### 3. Choosing Ideas that Surround the Central Concept

Student answers will vary. Verify that each concept around the central concept relates to the main concept directly. Also be sure that each main idea is in a box.

### 4. Showing the Relationships Between Ideas

Student answers will vary. Be sure that each line between boxes details the correct relationship between the concepts the line connects.

### 5. Expand your Concept Map

(See next page for explanation.)

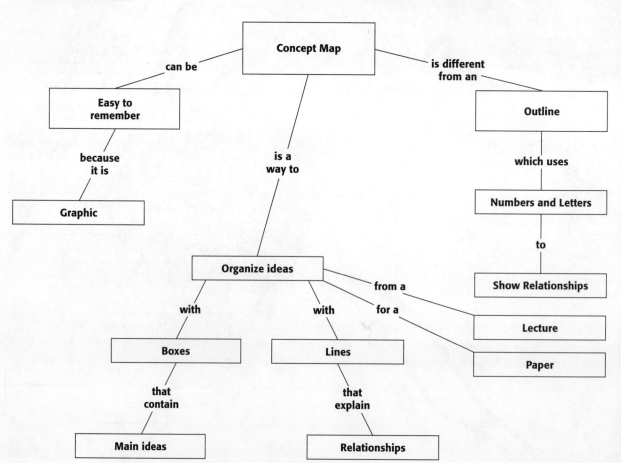

Student answers will vary. Be sure that each concept they listed in step one is included in a box, and that each line describes the relationship between the concepts it connects. One possible concept map for the introductory paragraphs is as shown on the previous page.

## 1.4 Compiling and Weighing Evidence

### 1. Compiling the Evidence

Some students may have additional items circled here. They should eliminate any such irrelevant facts or opinions in parts two and three.

A. A bowling ball falls to the Earth much faster than a feather.

C. In a vacuum, where there is no air resistance, a bowling ball and a feather dropped together have the same speed at any given height.

E. Air resistance depends on the shape of an object.

G. A crumpled-up sheet of paper falls to Earth faster than a flat sheet of paper.

### 2. Classifying the Evidence

Student classifications may vary in this chart, depending on their level of understanding at this point. The following is an example, but other variations are possible. All variations should be corrected in part three.

| Supports the theory | Contradicts the theory | Doesn't do either |
|---|---|---|
| In a vacuum, where there is no air resistance, a bowling ball and a feather dropped together have the same speed at any given height. | A bowling ball falls to the Earth much faster than a feather. | Air resistance depends on the shape of an object. |
| | A crumpled-up sheet of paper falls to Earth faster than a flat sheet of paper. | |

### 3. Considering Contradictory Evidence

| Supports the theory | Contradicts the theory |
|---|---|
| In a vacuum, where there is no air resistance, a bowling ball and a feather fall at exactly the same rate. | |
| A bowling ball falls to the Earth much faster than a feather. | |
| Two steel balls of different sizes and weights fall towards Earth at different rates. | |
| The amount of air resistance depends on the shape of an object. | |

### 4. Weighing the Evidence

Since there is no contradictory evidence, Galileo's theory is supported. The strongest support is the evidence that, in a vacuum, a bowling ball and a feather fall at exactly the same rate. Evidence that at first appears contradictory—a bowling ball and a feather fall at different rates in air—is accounted for by the fact that air resistance depends on the shape of an object. This is why a crumpled-up sheet of paper falls to Earth faster than a flat sheet of paper.

## 1.5 Forming A Hypothesis

### 1. Collecting Observations

Student answers may include:

- The plant has been knocked onto the floor each day for the past week.
- The plant is an aloe plant.
- The plant has doubled in size over the past year.
- The plant is left securely on the windowsill each day.
- Paw prints were left in the dirt.
- A tree that grew near the window was cut down a week ago.
- The cousin has played loud music with bass for the past week.

## 2. Evaluating the Observations

Observations which may lead to a possible solution include:

- Paw prints were left in the dirt.
- A tree that grew near the window was cut down a week ago.
- The cousin has played loud music with bass for the past week.

## 3. Imagining Possible Solutions

Student answers may vary. Be sure no possible solutions contradict any of the observations listed in step one. Possible solutions based on the given observations include:

- The cat may have been knocking the plant down each day.
- Without a tree to block the wind, the wind could be strong enough to knock the plant down.
- The vibrations from the cousin's loud music with bass could be so strong that they cause the windowsill to vibrate, which could knock the plant down.

## 4. Judging which Explanations are Hypotheses

Student answers may vary. Each possible solution listed above in step three could be disproved, and hence is a valid hypothesis. Any possible solutions which could never be disproved are not valid hypotheses.

# 1.6 Testing a Hypothesis

## 1. Presenting Hypotheses

**Hypothesis 1:** The cat has been knocking over the plant.

**Hypothesis 2:** The wind, no longer blocked by the tree, is now strong enough to knock the plant from the window sill.

**Hypothesis 3:** The cousin has been playing her music so loud that the vibrations have caused the plant to fall from the windowsill.

## 2. Making Predictions

Be sure that each prediction tests only the given hypothesis. Possible answers include:

**Predictions for 1:** If the first hypothesis is correct, and the door is shut so the cat cannot get into the room, the plant would not be knocked over.

**Predictions for 2:** If the second hypothesis is correct, and the window is shut each morning, the wind would not blow into the room, and the plant would not be knocked over.

**Predictions for 3:** If the third hypothesis is correct, and the cousin refrains from playing loud music, the plant would not be knocked over.

## 3. Designing Experiments

**Experiment to test hypothesis 1:** Shut the door in the morning, so that the cat cannot enter the room with the plant, and see if the plant is knocked over at the end of the day.

**Experiment to test hypothesis 2:** Close the window, so that the wind cannot blow into the room, and see if the plant is knocked over at the end of the day.

**Experiment to test hypothesis 3:** Ask your cousin to avoid playing her music for a day, and see if the plant is knocked over at the end of the day.

# 1.7 Classifying Items

## 1. Listing Each Category

pure substances, mixtures, elements, compounds, homogeneous, heterogeneous

## 2. Arranging the Categories

Most general categories: pure substances, mixtures

Subdivisions: elements and compounds are pure substances; homogeneous and heterogeneous are types of mixtures

## 3. Drawing the Diagram

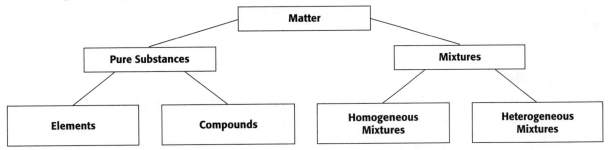

## 1.8 Reading to Evaluate and to Identify Bias

1. Answers will vary. Possible answers include:
- How many people actually die from DHMO inhalation each year, and how does this occur?
- How is skin damaged by solid DHMO?
- What is involved in DHMO dependency, and how many people does this problem affect?
- How does DHMO cause power failures?
- Does DHMO actually cause tumors, or does it just happen to be found in tumors?

2. Answers will vary. Possible answers include:
- How is DHMO good for nature?
- How could nature handle a DHMO accident?
- How does DHMO affect the balance of nature on our planet?
- How does DHMO help people grow?

3. Answers will vary, but students should realize that there is not enough evidence to make an informed judgment from the information presented.

   After assessing students' results, point out that the substance *dihydrogen monoxide* is actually just water. Have students reread the two selections with this fact in mind.

## 1.9 Evaluating Data

### 1. Plotting Data Points

Students should include a data point for each pair of measurements in the table, for a total of seven data points. Be sure that each height measurement corresponds to the $x$-axis, and each distance measurement to the $y$-axis.

### 2. Finding a Pattern/3. Showing the pattern

Students' graphs should depict a straight line that begins at the origin and has a slope of approximately $\frac{3}{2}$. The line should pass through or close to all data points except one (height = 60 cm, distance = 85 cm).

### 4. Evaluating Data

Students should observe that all data points except one fall on or close to the straight line. Since there is only one error out of seven measurements, the data is acceptable; it can be assumed that the one anomalous data point is due to experimental error.

## 2.1 Significant Figures

1. 578.7 m, 47.33 kg, 789.5 cm
2. 3155.2 m, 8.7777 cm, 93.7556 kg
3. 183 cm$^2$
4. 120 kg•m/s$^2$ (3 significant figures)
5. 170 m$^3$

## 2.2 Scientific Notation

1. $2 \times 10^4$ Hz, $1.5 \times 10^5$ Hz
2. $5 \times 10^{-3}$ cm/h, $2 \times 10^{-2}$ cm/h
3. $1.66 \times 10^8$ km$^2$, $4.2 \times 10^3$ m
4. 1470 m/s
5. 0.000 000 01 cm

## 2.3 Dimensional Analysis

1. no
2. yes
3. yes

## 2.4 SI Units and Conversions Between Them

1. 0.100 km
2. $5.98 \times 10^{30}$ mg
3. W
4. $4.448 \times 10^5$ g • cm/s$^2$
5. $6.67 \times 10^{-17}$ N • km$^2$/g$^2$

## 2.5 Converting between U.S. Conventional and SI Measurements

1. 47 miles/hour
2. 13 liters
3. 91.4 meters

## 3.1 Ratios and Proportions

1. 6 cups of water
2. 21 male teachers
3. $x = 600$

## 3.2 Percentages

1. 62%; 44%; friend's neighborhood
2. 52%; 49%; ninth grade class
3. $\frac{3}{5}$
4. $\frac{12}{25}$

## 3.3 Balancing Chemical Equations

1. No; the equation is not balanced because there are 2 N atoms on the left side and 1 N atoms on the right side, and 4 O atoms on the left side and 2 O atoms on the right side.
2. $2H_2 + O_2 \rightarrow 2H_2O$
3. $CH_4 + 2O_2 \rightarrow CO_2 + 2H_2O$

## 3.4 Squares and Square Roots

1. 37 m$^2$
2. 10.51 m
3. 36.4444

## 3.5 Operations with Exponents

1. $b = a^9$
2. $x = y$
3. $y = x$
4. $y = x$

## 3.6 Rates of Change

1. 30 weeks (2 significant figures)
2. 15 weeks (2 significant figures)
3. 5 seconds
4. 4 seconds

## 4.1 How to Round Numbers

1. 200
2. 7600; 7600
3. 332

## 4.2 Ordering Multiple Operations

1. 34
2. 267
3. 84
4. 4
5. 821

## 4.3 Entering Exponents

1. 1 953 125 cm$^3$
2. 166 375 km$^3$
3. 0.0001 kg

## 5.1 Angles and Degrees

1. 30°
2. 50°
3. yes
4. 360°

## 5.2 The Area of a Circle

1. 491 cm$^2$
2. 200 m$^2$ (2 significant figures)

## 5.3 Surface Area

1. 38 000 000 km$^2$
2. 7350 cm$^2$

## 5.4 The Volume of a Sphere

1. 221 000 cm$^3$
2. $1.09 \times 10^{15}$ km$^3$

## 5.5 Rearranging Algebraic Equations

1. $l = A/w$
2. $t = d/v$
3. $w = V/(l \times h)$
4. $\Delta t = E/(cm)$

## 5.6 Equations Involving a Constant

1. $4.0 \times 10^{-7}$ m
2. 170 kg•m/s$^2$, or 170 N

## 5.7 Equations with Three Parts

1. 450 N
2. 6

## 6.1 Making and Interpreting Tables

### 1. Determining what data should go into the table

The following data should go into the table: Monday: 6 fashion magazines, 2 sports magazines; Tuesday: 6 fashion magazines, 3 sports magazines; Wednesday: 8 fashion magazines, 5 sports magazines; Thursday: 6 fashion magazines, 3 sports magazines; Friday: 2 fashion magazines, 4 sports magazines; Saturday: 3 fashion magazines, 1 sports magazine; Sunday: 2 fashion magazines, 1 sports magazine.

### 2. Determining how the table will be organized

Categories: Monday, Tuesday, Wednesday, Thursday, Friday, Saturday, Sunday (one group); Fashion magazines, Sports magazines (another group)

### 3. Making the table and filling in the data

Students' completed tables should be similar to the following:

|  | Fashion magazines | Sports magazines |
|---|---|---|
| Monday | 6 | 2 |
| Tuesday | 6 | 3 |
| Wednesday | 8 | 5 |
| Thursday | 6 | 3 |
| Friday | 2 | 4 |
| Saturday | 3 | 1 |
| Sunday | 2 | 1 |

### 4. Interpreting the data in the table

**a.** Wednesday

**b.** fashion magazines

**c.** fewer

## 6.2 Making a Line Graph

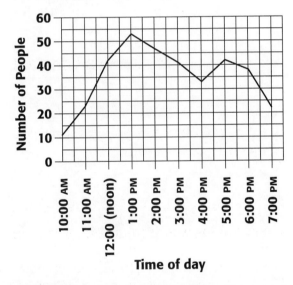

### 6.3 Making and Interpreting Bar and Pie Graphs

1. August
2. drama
3. 25%

### 1. Making a Bar Graph

Students' bar graphs should have each month listed on the horizontal axis, and a scale from 0 to 5 on the vertical axis. The horizontal and vertical axes should be labeled "Months" and "Number of Movies Seen," respectively. The heights for each bar should be as follows: Jan: 3, Feb: 2, Mar: 1, Apr: 1, May: 3, June: 4, July: 5, Aug: 4, Sep: 2, Oct: 2, Nov: 0, Dec: 4.

### 2. Making a Pie Graph

Students' pie graphs should have five pieces labeled action, drama, comedy, romance, and documentary. The relative sizes of the pieces should be approximately as follows: action 42%; drama 25%; comedy 22%; romance 10%. (Total does not add up to 100% due to rounding.) The exact size of each piece is not as significant as the relative sizes between pieces, for example comedy should be slightly smaller than drama, action should be the largest, etc.

## 6.4 Deciding Which Type of Graph Is Appropriate

1. line or bar graph
2. pie graph
3. bar graph or line graph

## 6.5 Slope of a Line

1. $\frac{1}{5}$

2. $\frac{0.6}{3.0}$ or $\frac{0.2}{1.0}$

3. speed

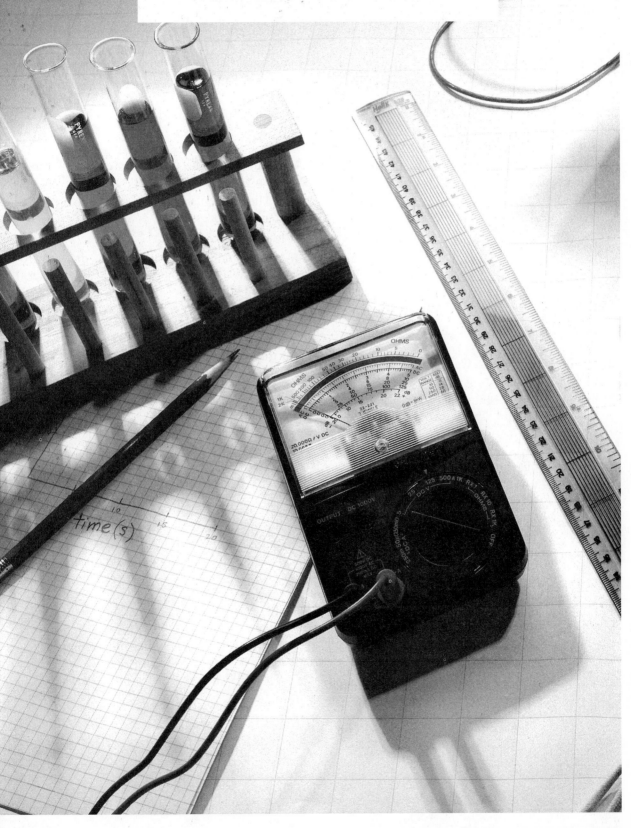

# LESSON FOCUS
# ANSWER KEY

# LESSON FOCUS TRANSPARENCIES

## LT 1

1. Answers will vary but may include physics, the study of the physical world; chemistry, the study of matter and how it changes; biology, the study of living things; ecology, the study of how living things interact with each other and with their nonliving environments; geology, the study of the physical nature and history of the earth; and astronomy, the study of the universe.

2. Answers will vary but may include television, radio, airplanes, telecommunications, applied genetics, and biotechnologies.

3. the law of conservation of mass, the law of conservation of energy

## LT 2

1. a. N
   b. Y
   c. N
   d. N
   e. Y
   f. Y
   g. Y
   h. N

2. fertilizer, plants, soil, water, scale, gardening tools, ruler, measuring cup

3. height of plants, centimeters; amount of fertilizer, grams; amount of water, milliliters

## LT 3

1. 25 g of fertilizer

2. 0 g of fertilizer

3. Graphs will vary depending on their scales. Students should plot amount of fertilizer on the x-axis and plant height on the y-axis, as shown on the graph below.

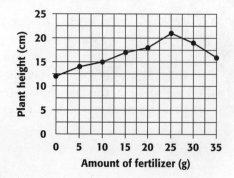

4. Generally, plant height increases as more fertilizer is added to the plants.

## LT 4

1. a. magnesium
   b. bromine
   c. nitrogen
   d. sulfur
   e. calcium
   f. boron
   g. zinc
   h. silicon
   i. neon

2. sodium, potassium, iron, silver

## LT 5

1. b; The molecules in this drawing are in uniformly fixed positions.

2. c; The molecules in this drawing seem to be easily compressible.

3. liquid (a), solid (b)

4. c; The random molecules in this drawing exist in mostly empty space, and they are not in contact with one another.

## LT 6

1. First separate the iron filings from the mixture using a magnet.

2. Add water to the sand and sugar mixture so that the sugar dissolves. Then filter the mixture to isolate the sand.

3. Boil the mixture of sugar and water to isolate the sugar.

## LT 7

1. Answers will vary. Two people are each wearing at least one sneaker. They are playing basketball. One shoots the ball at the goal. The other, who is wearing shorts, attempts to block the ball from entering the goal.

2. Answers will vary but may include blocks of the picture indicating whether the two people are playing basketball at a park or in a gym, blocks of the picture indicating whether or not the two people are playing alone, and blocks of the picture indicating whether the two people are playing for sport or for recreation.

## LT 8

1. Accept any answers for this item that match a consistent scheme described in student answers for item 2. One possibility is described below.

   **Category 1** Computer World, Family Computing, All About Computing, How to Use the Internet, Building a Web Site

   **Category 2** Beautiful Homes, Home Decorating, Modern Housekeeping, Home Makers Magazine

   **Category 3** Car Trends, Classic Cars, Easy Car Repairs, The Sports Car Story

   **Category 4** The Healthy Man, Homeopathic Medicine, The Healthy Woman, The Health Newsletter, Good Nutrition

   **Category 5** Auto Racing, Sporting Times, Sports and Scores, Golf for Everyone, Football Stories, Tennis Tips

   **Category 6** Calling All Girls, Child's Play, Calling All Boys, Nursery Rhymes, Read Aloud Stories

2. similarity in content
3. Answers will vary depending on initial groupings.

## LT 9

1. **a.** gas, molecules only
   **b.** gas, atoms only
   **c.** liquid, atoms only
   **d.** gas, atoms and molecules
   **e.** liquid, atoms and molecules
   **f.** solid, atoms and molecules
   **g.** solid, atoms only
   **h.** liquid, molecules only
   **i.** gas, atoms only

2. d, i

## LT 10

1. 4 sticks of butter per pound, 12 eggs per dozen, 5 sticks of gum per pack, 2 shoes per pair, 500 sheets of paper per ream, 52 cards per deck

2. Six sticks of butter is equivalent to one and one-half pounds of butter, which can be measured from the large block of butter using the scale.

## LT 11

1. Each molecule contains three atoms, at least one of which is oxygen.

2. The carbon dioxide molecule has two oxygen atoms on its ends, but the water molecule has an oxygen atom in the middle of the molecule. The angles between the atoms of each molecule are different.

## LT 12

1. The left flower lost a petal. The right flower gained a petal.

2. The left flower became positively charged. The right flower became negatively charged.

3. The opposite charges will attract each other.

## LT 13

1. where large atoms are bonded together
2. where large and small atoms are bonded together
3. more force or energy

## LT 14

1. b, d, e, g, h
2. They are all living things.
3. Carbon forms covalent bonds.

## LT 15

1. energy
2.

|          | Before | After |
|----------|--------|-------|
| Carbon   | 1      | 1     |
| Hydrogen | 4      | 4     |
| Oxygen   | 4      | 4     |

3. They are equal. This demonstrates the law of conservation of mass.

4. There is more energy stored in the bonds among the atoms before the reaction.

## LT 16

1. b
2. c
3. d
4. a

## LT 17

1. Model B has the same number of atoms on each side, but model A does not.

2. In model A, some atoms are not accounted for, according to the law of conservation of mass.

3. Changing the subscript on the product indicates that the product is a compound other than water.

## LT 18

1. c
2. Small sticks used as kindling catch fire more quickly than larger logs.
3. Atoms of liquid zinc at its melting point will react faster with HCl.

## LT 19

**1.–5.** Answers will vary. Be sure each is a mixture with its components listed.

**6.** All mixtures could be classified by uniformity of composition.

## LT 20

**1.** The sugar dissolves more quickly before ice is added. If ice is added first, the sugar does not dissolve as quickly.

**2.** It settles at the bottom of the glass.

**3.** The bottom of the tea or lemonade is sweeter than the rest.

**4.** Stir the tea or lemonade to help the sugar on the bottom of the glass dissolve.

## LT 21

**1.** acid

**2.** base

**3.** base

**4.** acid

**5.** base

**6.** Possible answers include that acids are sour tasting and that they hurt an open cut.

**7.** Possible answers include that bases are not sour tasting and that they are slippery when dissolved in water.

## LT 22

**1.** A particularly sour green apple is due to an excess of acid.

**2.** Baking soda is a base.

**3.** These chemicals in the stomach are acids.

**4.** Drain cleaners that contain lye are bases.

**5.** Most dirt on windows is slightly acidic.

## LT 23

**1.** Black circles represent neutrons. White circles represent protons. The entire cluster is a nucleus.

**2.**

| Atom | Protons | Neutrons |
|------|---------|----------|
| $^{32}_{15}P$ | 15 | 17 |
| $^{60}_{27}Co$ | 27 | 33 |
| $^{14}_{7}N$ | 7 | 7 |
| $^{23}_{11}Na$ | 11 | 12 |
| $^{32}_{16}S$ | 16 | 16 |
| $^{210}_{84}Po$ | 84 | 126 |

## LT 24

**1.** b

**2.** a

**3.** a; It forms larger atoms.

## LT 25

**1.** Energy is released.

**2.** Gamma radiation is likely to pass through the body more easily.

**3.** Alpha radiation was used because it is massive and able to collide with the gold atoms.

## LT 26

**1. a.** time
   **b.** distance
   **c.** time
   **d.** speed
   **e.** distance

**2. a.** s
   **b.** m
   **c.** s
   **d.** m/s
   **e.** m

## LT 27

**1. a.** a change in velocity due to a change in speed
   **b.** no change in speed or direction of motion, so no change in velocity
   **c.** a change in velocity due to changes in both speed and direction of motion
   **d.** a change in velocity due to a change in the direction of motion

**2.** Its velocity will increase in the direction the student pulls it with the rope.

## LT 28

**1.** The marble rolls down the ramp due to the force of gravity.

**2.** The marble keeps rolling because no force is exerted on it until it strikes the front of the wagon.

**3.** The crumpled piece of paper would reach the floor first. The difference in surface area between these two pieces of paper accounts for the different forces on each one.

## LT 29

**1.** d

**2.** The person exerts a force on the wall, and the wall exerts an equal and opposite force on the person. The force increases to match the increased force of the person.

# LT 30

1. The fulcrum of a door is along its hinges.
2. Pushing near the side farthest from the hinges requires the least force to open a door.
3. The doorstop will work best near the side farthest from the hinges.

# LT 31

1. The sun's energy is captured by plants, which are eaten as food. This food provides a release of energy for other uses, such as swinging the bat.
2. Yes, because the ball moves a distance in response to the force.
3. The energy is absorbed in the glove and hand of the fielder. Some energy is also released as sound when the fielder catches the ball.

# LT 32

1. The sled has the most potential energy at the top of the hill and the least potential energy at the bottom of the hill.
2. The sled has the most kinetic energy at the bottom of the hill and the least kinetic energy at the top of the hill.
3. The potential energy decreases, the kinetic energy increases, but the total energy remains the same.
4. This energy is transformed into heat by the friction between the runners of the sled and the snow.

# LT 33

1. Bowl A would feel cold; bowl B would feel warm.
2. Bowl A would feel warm; bowl B would feel cold.
3. A more effective way to describe the weather would be to give average temperature ranges.

# LT 34

1. The tin cup may get hot enough to burn your lips. The hot, fast-moving molecules in the cocoa collide with the atoms in the cup, making them move faster and raising the cup's temperature.
2. The warm air near the candle rises because its molecules move fast and are far apart, so the air is less dense. When the hot, fast-moving atoms and molecules strike molecules in the hand, they transfer energy to it.

3. The radiation from the fire travels in all directions, not just upward.

# LT 35

1. The area near the liquid will get cooler as evaporation occurs.
2. Because the area near the thermostat was cooler due to evaporation, the thermostat signalled the heater to keep running.
3. a. no
   b. no
   c. yes
   d. no
   e. yes

# LT 36

1. Small concentric circles radiate out from where the rock entered the water. Energy was transferred from the rock to the water.
2. The energy comes from the wave itself. The water wave is energy traveling through the water.
3. The string vibrates back and forth very quickly.
4. The musician touches the cymbals with his or her body to stop the vibration.

# LT 37

1. Answers will vary but may include AM radio (radio waves), FM radio (radio waves), microwave ovens (microwaves), X rays in medicine (X rays), night-vision goggles (infrared), and telescopes (visible light, microwaves, and radio waves).
2. Answers will vary. A laser is accurately focused to burn away an unwanted area. Blood vessels are sealed in the process due to the intensely focused energy. In this way a patient receives a virtually bloodless surgery.

# LT 38

1. Light waves strike the flat surface of a mirror and bounce back. Since the surface is flat, the light waves are reflected back at equal angles of incidence, producing an image.
2. Answers will vary. The reflection of sunlight off the mirror makes it easier to find a lost hiker.
3. Sound waves are bounced off surfaces, such as walls, buildings, or canyon walls, and are returned, creating an echo.
4. Light waves hit the blinds and are reflected. The angle of reflection of the light waves depends on the angle of the blinds.

## LT 39

1. Sound waves travel most quickly through a solid since the molecules of a solid are closest together. Sound waves travel slightly slower through a liquid than through a solid, and sound waves travel the slowest through a gas since the molecules of a gas are farthest apart.

2. Different musical notes are made with a wind instrument by varying the length of its air chamber, which varies the length of the wave produced.

3. Various musical notes are made with a string instument by pushing different strings down tightly along the neck of the instrument. This lengthens or shortens the wavelength of the standing wave produced.

4. In both types of instruments, various sounds are made by changing the wavelength of the standing wave produced by the instrument.

## LT 40

1. The components of visible light are separated by wavelength when light passes through a prism. The various colors that make up visible light are then clearly visible.

2. Water droplets in the sky act like tiny prisms, separating sunlight into its composite wavelengths.

3. Stealth airplanes have low profiles, which allow most radio waves to pass around the airplane. Some waves do hit the airplane, but the airplane is made of a reinforced composite material that absorbs radio waves instead of reflecting them. If a sound wave is not reflected, then the airplane cannot be detected by radar.

4. Gamma waves carry more energy than radio waves do. Gamma rays carry enough energy to destroy living cells.

## LT 41

1. Answers will vary but may include telescopes, microscopes, cameras, lasers, and medical instruments.

2. The mirror is used to focus light behind the object and up through the lens so that the object can be clearly seen through the microscope.

3. Answers will vary but may include that fluorescent orange is used for safety vests and that red, green, and yellow are used as traffic signals.

4. White would feel cooler because it reflects light energy, while black absorbs it.

## LT 42

1. Answers will vary but may include magnifying glasses, telescopes, microscopes, cameras, and eyeglasses.

2. A curved mirror gives a wider field of vision.

3. These mirrors are in the shape of a spherical cap so that they provide a wider field of vision. But that distorts the sizes of images, making them seem smaller and farther away.

4. Mirrors with various shaped surfaces are used to focus the light rays to give the desired effects.

## LT 43

1. Answers will vary but may include clean hair being combed, clothes coming out of the dryer, plastic food wrap being used, nylon warm-up suits and jackets being worn, and a person walking across a carpeted floor.

2. Extra electrons are rubbed off some articles of clothing onto others. The clothes are then unbalanced in charge.

3. Electrons are rubbed off carpet onto the person walking across the carpet. The person then carries a charge instead of being neutrally charged.

4. Like electric charges repel and unlike electric charges attract, just like the poles of a magnet.

## LT 44

1. Answers will vary but may include CD players, radios, video games, flashlights, and telephones.

2. Copper is a good conductor of electricity, it has an acceptable rate of energy loss, it is safe, and it is inexpensive.

3. Pulling on the electric cord can break the copper wire inside the cord. This causes the cord to stop conducting the electric current.

4. Tap water is a good conductor of electricity. Using one of these appliances in or around water can result in the electric current flowing from the appliance through the water and into you, possibly delivering a fatal jolt of electricity.

## LT 45

1. Answers will vary, but all devices listed must require electricity.

2. The lights are wired in a series circuit instead of a parallel circuit.

3. The circuit overloaded, causing the circuit breaker to trip. Correct this by turning off some of the appliances and resetting the circuit breaker. Another option is to install a new fuse.

## LT 46

1. Answers will vary but may include refrigerator magnets, refrigerator door seals, cabinet door latches, compasses, and hand tools.

2. The two magnets will either attract each other or repel each other. A 180° rotation will produce the opposite of the initial result.

3. A compass points to the magnetic north pole, which is near the geographic North Pole, giving a disoriented person a sense of direction.

4. No, the magnetic N pole and geographic North Pole are two different geographic locations. The magnetic S pole is located near the geographic North Pole.

## LT 47

1. Answers will vary but may include fans, computers, aquarium pumps, refrigerators, washing machines, hand drills, and electric screw drivers.

2. A shaft in an electric motor is designed so that one magnet is attracted to two other magnets. Two magnets are located opposite each other and their poles are constantly shifted. The magnet located in the center of these two magnets will be initially attracted to one of the magnets and then repulsed because of the pole change. The constant attraction-repulsion of the center magnet will cause the shaft to rotate.

3. The magnetic domains within the needle temporarily align making the needle a temporary magnet.

## LT 48

1. Answers will vary but may include CD players, boom boxes, and tape recorders.

2. Answers will vary but may include hairdryers, curling irons, electric razors, and electric fans.

3. The CD player is designed to use direct current. The adapter takes the household alternating current and converts it to direct current.

4. The voltage that goes into a neighborhood is dangerously high for a single home. The voltage must be decreased for safety reasons.

## LT 49

1. Answers will vary but may include sending messages by secret codes.

2. A satellite dish is required to collect the wave signal that is transmitted by the satellite.

3. Satellites provide speed, availability, and reliability in our communication system without requiring the use of breakable wires.

## LT 50

1. Radios, televisions, and telephones are designed to pick up a particular signal. We can adjust which signal is picked up by changing the channel or tuning the devise.

2. The radio signal becomes unclear when it is not properly tuned in and when it is out of range. Fine tuning the tuning knob may correct the problem.

3. In the early days of the telephone, there were no electronic switches to select the correct phone number being dialed. This had to be done manually by operators.

## LT 51

1. Answers will vary. The list may include finding books at the library, registering for classes in the counselor's office, checking out of school in the attendance office, making a deposit at the bank, buying food at the grocery store, or researching on the Internet at home.

2. Answers will vary. The list may include MS Word, MSWorks, Adobe Illustrator, Math Blaster, and Netscape Navigator.

3. The Internet is a network of computers connected together to exchange information. The Internet provides a low-cost worldwide information-exchange network.

4. Answers will vary. The Internet provides an easy and inexpensive method of sharing resource information, such as research findings.

## LT 52

1. Answers will vary but may include stars, planets, comets, asteroids, black holes, and galaxies. The students may also include the names of individual heavenly bodies.

2. The basic force that holds the solar system together is the force of gravity.

3. Both the solar system and the universe are held together by gravity.

4. The universe is ordered and predictable at almost every scale. The positions of planets in the night sky have been known for centuries. The predicted appearance of comets, such as Halley's comet, which only becomes visible about every 76 years, has been foretold for centuries. (The appearance of Halley's comet varies within a small range because the gravitational pull of the other planets affects its orbit.) Planets orbit the sun, and stars orbit the center of the galaxy. The universe as a whole is expanding in a predictable manner.

## LT 53

1. Answers will vary. The list may include Aries, Taurus, Gemini, Cancer, Leo, Virgo, Libra, Scorpius, Sagittarius, Capricornus, Aquarius, Pisces, Cassiopeia, Orion, and Pegasus.

2. Each type of wave gives additional information about this complex puzzle called the universe. By connecting various pieces of information, a clearer picture of the universe emerges.

3. The same elements should be found throughout the universe because all of the components of the universe began from the same source, according to the big bang theory.

## LT 54

1. Answers will vary but should include six of the following planets: Mercury, Venus, Earth, Mars, Jupiter, Saturn, Uranus, Neptune, and Pluto.

2. Answers will vary. The planets are composed of some of the same elements. The inner planets—Mercury, Venus, Earth, and Mars—and Pluto have solid surfaces. The outer planets—Jupiter, Saturn, Uranus, and Neptune—are composed of gases.

3. Answers will vary. Some people have the desire to understand how the universe and its contents came to be.

## LT 55

1. The outer layer of the peach is thin and relatively hard, like Earth's crust.

2. The pulp is softer and part liquid, just like the somewhat molten mantle.

3. Like the pit, Earth's core is solid and dense.

## LT 56

1. The pressure inside the bottle will increase.

2. Eventually the pressure exceeds the force of the bottle's walls causing the bottle to explode.

3. When the hot molten material breaks through the crust, one possible result is a volcano.

## LT 57

**Granite:** large crystals, light color
**Basalt:** small crystals, dark color
**Obsidian:** hard, dark, glasslike, no obvious crystal structure, dark color
**Sandstone:** fine-grained with layers, small crystals, light color

## LT 58

1. A wave has energy that allows it to move sand as it rolls onto a beach.

2. The Colorado River made the Grand Canyon by weathering away the land over time.

3. Answers will vary but may include ice, wind, plants, and chemicals.

4. Potholes form in the road as a result of continuous wearing by cars and trucks.

## LT 59

Answers will vary but should reflect that this is an exercise in creative writing. Some students may know more about the greenhouse effect than others. Accept paragraphs with evidence of creative ideas about the differences in Earth's conditions as a result of significantly higher or lower temperatures. Dramatic increases or decreases in temperature would affect Earth's climate, changing weather patterns by bringing droughts to some areas and floods to others. A significant increase in temperature could cause icecaps to melt and ocean levels to rise. A significant decrease in temperature could cause the formation of even larger icecaps. Geological aspects of Earth would change as a result of changes in weathering. Encourage students to imagine ways that plant and animal life on Earth would adapt to changes in temperature by evolving to withstand the extreme heat or cold.

## LT 60

1. Barometer (b) has a higher column due to greater atmospheric pressure.

2. Barometer (a) is likely to be at the top of a mountain (lower pressure) and (b) at sea level (higher pressure).

3. Atmospheric pressure increases as altitude decreases. Barometer (a) measures a lower atmospheric pressure than barometer (b), so barometer (a) is more likely to be at the top of a mountain.

## LT 61

1. Yes. The longer days occur because the Northern Hemisphere faces toward the sun, leading to hotter days.

2. Answers will vary. Climate descriptions should be general rather than specific.

3. Mountains can block winds and can force moist air upward, causing precipitation.

## LT 62

1. These organisms would die fairly quickly. These organisms have adapted to their original environments, where all of their needs are met.

2. Colonists were very dependent upon the environment for their survival. If their crops did not grow well, they starved. Colonists had to use whatever they could find to build shelters. Colonists did not have a transportation system. Ships brought supplies from Europe, but it took months to make the trip across the Atlantic.

3. No, we are not. Supplies can be transported in from other areas. We also have better methods of surviving natural disasters.

## LT 63

1. Answers may include electricity, natural gas, coal, heating oil, solar energy, geothermal energy, kerosene, and wood.

2. Natural gas, coal, heating oil, and kerosene are all fossil fuels. Electricity is often made from burning fossil fuels. Natural gas, coal, heating oil, and kerosene are all nonrenewable resources. Solar and geothermal energy are both renewable resources.

3. All living organisms use the food they consume as an energy source. All organisms are dependent upon the sun for a food supply. Organisms either make their own food through photosynthesis or eat organisms that have made their food from photosynthesis.

## LT 64

1. Answers will vary but may include waste, air, water, and thermal pollution.

2. Reduce the amount of trash we produce by eliminating single-use, or disposable, items. Require manufacturing facilities to clean up air and water emissions. Require manufacturing facilities to release waste water at ambient temperature. Reduce the number of automobiles used daily and improve the emissions of those cars on the roads.

3. There is no market for the recycled item. The cost of recycling the item is too much to produce an affordable product. Recycling is inconvenient and the public may not always participate.

## LT 65

Answers will vary. Check to be sure menus are well-balanced according to the food pyramid.

## LT 66

1. maintaining body temperature, respiration, digestion of food, blood filtering, body repair and growth, waste removal

2. A Calorie measures the amount of energy contained in food. It is defined as the amount of energy required to warm 1 kg of water by 1°C.

3. An apple contains vitamins and minerals that are needed to maintain good health. An apple is low in fat content too. A chocolate candy bar, however, contains few valuable nutrients and is extremely high in sugar content.

4. The food label contains the following types of information: serving size, number of servings per container, number of Calories, number of Calories from fat, total amount of fat, amount of saturated fat, amount of cholesterol, amount of sodium, total amount of carbohydrates, amount of dietary fiber, amount of sugar, amount of protein, and types and amounts of vitamins.

## LT 67

1. Breaking food into smaller pieces creates more surface area, allowing more contact with the digestive fluids in the mouth and stomach.

2. The smell of the food triggers the release of saliva into your mouth. Saliva contains enzymes that begin the digestive process. Your body is preparing for the digestion of food.

3. **Teeth** Teeth tear and grind food.
   **Stomach** Ground food mixes with digestive fluids (hydrochloric acid and pepsin) in the stomach.
   **Small intestine** The small intestine provides a location with a suitable pH for enzymes to continue the breakdown of food. The small intestine also absorbs nutrients into the body.

## LT 68

1. Blood carries nutrients to the cells and removes waste materials from the cells. The blood also contains white blood cells, which enable the body to fight against bacteria and other disease causing pathogens.
2. If blood did not clot, a person could bleed to death from a minor wound. A clot also keeps disease causing organisms out of the wound.
3. Hemophilia is a blood disorder that prevents the clotting of blood. Minor cuts or bruises can be fatal for hemophiliacs because they can easily bleed to death.

## LT 69

1. The air that a person inhales must contain oxygen. The cells in the body need oxygen to undergo the breakdown of food at the cellular level. Without a constant supply of oxygen, permanent brain damage or death will occur within a few minutes. Similarly, it is necessary to remove carbon dioxide from the body.
2. If a person stops breathing the cells do not receive the oxygen required for the cell to live; therefore, the cells begin to die. When large numbers of cells die in the brain, permanent brain damage or death will occur within minutes.
3. Answers will vary but may include slow rate: sleeping or relaxed; medium rate: breathing normally; and fast rate: frightened or strenuously active.

## LT 70

1. Smoking has been linked to the following diseases: atherosclerosis, high blood pressure, emphysema, bronchitis, asthma, and cancer of the lungs, mouth, throat, larynx, esophagus, bladder, pancreas, and kidneys.
2. Answers will vary.
3. Answers will vary.

## LT 71

1. Answers will vary. We would not be able to walk, so we would need a different form of locomotion. Our methods of acquiring food would have to be different too.
2. Joints give us freedom of movement. The human body contains five different types of joints that allow different types of movement. We would not be able to sit, stand, or walk without the ability to bend our legs and arms at movable joints.
3. Muscles can be strengthened by eating a balanced diet and by exercising.

## LT 72

1. Exercise is important to keep a person healthy. A person that is forced to live in a bed or sit in a wheelchair will lose strength if some exercise is not provided for his or her muscles.
2. One common health problem that results from not getting enough exercise is weight gain. The body must try to accommodate extra weight, straining the heart, muscles, bones, and other vital organs. It is not uncommon for an overweight person to have high blood pressure, diabetes, and frequent muscle strains due to the increased load.
3. Lifting weights builds strength and endurance in muscles.
4. The athlete may become injured because his or her body is not prepared for the extra stress of the activity.

## LT 73

1. Answers will vary but may include problems eating, drinking, walking, and working.
2. An astronaut's body will be stressed in space. It is important that the astronaut's body is able to adjust to conditions in space. It is also important that the astronaut is healthy before beginning the trip because there is limited medical care that can be given in space.
3. The astronaut's muscles weaken since there are fewer forces working in opposition to them.

## LT 74

1. Hand washing is a fundamental and effective way to control the spread of bacteria and viruses that cause illness among individuals.
2. Answers will vary. Possible ways to spread illness include through contact of body fluids and contact with contaminated water, food, or air.
3. Answers will vary. A person should not eat or drink after another person. People should not share make-up, toothbrushes, combs, hairbrushes, or other personal items. Washing your hands frequently will also help control the spread of illness.

## LT 75

1. During a disaster, such as a major earthquake, the drinking water supply becomes contaminated. Often, sewage systems rupture and are inoperable. Raw sewage mixes with the drinking water and flows through the streets. Diseases can easily spread through contaminated drinking water and contaminated public spaces. People are often left homeless and without a safe food supply. Contaminated food will cause the spread of illness. If there are many casualties, the removal of bodies from the living space must be done before their decaying also prompts the spread of diseases.

2. The food and water supplies are not as closely regulated in those countries as they are in the United States. Diseases and parasites are easily transferred through food and water.

3. These diseases have become obsolete because of the development of immunizations and aggressive immunization requirements for children in developed countries. In undeveloped countries where immunizations are not common, these diseases have reappeared.

## LT 76

1. Answers will vary. Some of the conditions include headaches, sinus pressure, minor aches and pains, upset stomach, diarrhea, allergies, runny nose, menstrual discomfort, and fever.

2. The federal government controls the sale of legal drugs in the United States. Drugs must meet federal guidelines and pass tests before they can be sold over the counter to the general public.

3. Answers will vary.

## LT 77

1. Reproductive organs provide the means to propogate the species.

2. Answers will vary. The young mother's body will take nutrients needed for the health of her body and contribute them to the baby's development. This will put the mother's health at risk. The baby will not get all of the nutrients needed for its development because the mother does not have them. Babies of such young mothers are usually born with low birth weights. The mothers are also at risk financially. In most cases, the government or family members must give the financial assistance needed for the survival of both the mother and her child.

3. Answers will vary but may include HIV, genital herpes, genital warts, gonorrhea, hepatitis B, and syphilis.

## LT 78

1. It is important for the survival of the fetus that there are no defects in the sperm. The sperm contains one half of the genetic material needed for the development of the baby. If the sperm is defective the survival of the baby may be at risk.

2. The fallopian tubes are not designed to stretch to accommodate the developing embryo. The fallopian tubes can rupture causing health risks or death to the mother and developing embryo.

3. The developing baby's nutritional needs must be met or the baby will not develop properly. The developing baby will also take some of its requirements from the mother's body. If the nutritional requirements for both mother and child are not being met, both will suffer. In addition, if the mother takes over-the-counter medication or takes illegal drugs, the developing baby will also be affected. An unborn baby is totally dependent upon the mother for all of its nutritional needs.

## LT 79

1. Answers will vary but should include changes in the body due to puberty.

2. Answers will vary. Many people choose to bottle-feed because of the stigma attached to breast-feeding in this country. Some women who are working outside of the home also choose to bottle-feed for the sake of convenience.

3. Answers will vary but should include an unwanted pregnancy and/or a sexually transmitted disease.

4. Answers will vary. Examples include babies born addicted to drugs, babies born with fetal alcohol syndrome, and babies born with birth defects related to the use of thalidomide.